A Primer on Renewable Energy

Howard C. Hayden

Library of Congress Control Number (LCCN): 2009939593

Hayden, Howard C.
A Primer on Renewable Energy

Includes bibliographic references
ISBN   13-digit: **978-0-9819694-1-1**

1.   Renewable Energy
2.   Solar Energy
3.   Wind Energy

Cover design by Brian Dunbar

Vales Lake Publishing, LLC
P.O. Box 7609
Pueblo West, CO 81007-0609
SAN: 2 5 4 - 2 5 3

Preface

Physics, we are often told, is dry enough to be a fire hazard. Physics underlies absolutely everything about renewable energy. One would suppose, therefore, that renewable energy must be boring beyond belief.

Nothing could be further from the truth. Solar energy, which is only part of the picture of renewable energy, inspires passion, enthusiasm, and devotion.

If our energy is to be supplied by renewable energy sources, we must understand two completely independent subjects: renewable energy *per se*, and our consumption of energy. That is, we must understand how we use energy, how much energy we use, and what role renewable energy sources might play.

The problem boils down to numbers. Just as it takes a bigger kitchen and more potatoes to feed a regiment than to feed a family, it takes more energy to run a nation than to run a household. Similarly, the solar collectors on a calculator are fine for the purpose, but those little things are obviously inadequate to run a steel mill. One needs to know *how much*.

Personal Disclaimer

I have some personal ties to the energy industry in the past, and a recent one. I once shoveled coal into gunnysacks for 5 cents per 100-pound sack. That was my dad's way of having me earn my own candy money. Nevertheless, the fifty cents I earned was all the money I ever received from the energy industry.

My academic research mostly involved accelerators. Once, while a university lawyer held up the purchase of some components for 14 months over some utter inanity, I worked with the Electrical Insulation Research group, studying high-voltage breakdown. They paid for my gasoline once so I could drive from Connecticut to New York to descend into some manholes. I learned how Brooklyners pronounce "oil in the joints": *earl in the jernts*.

Things have improved. I have served as an advisor on the Technical Advisory Group for Colorado Springs Utilities along with several other people representing a wide variety of opinions. At one meeting, I got a free can of soda pop.

TABLE OF CONTENTS

Table of Figures

Chapter 1   Introduction

All activity involves energy. Every year, the US consumes about one-fourth of the energy used in the world. Eighty-five percent of the energy used in the US comes from coal, oil, and natural gas. Only seven percent of our[1] energy comes from sources normally called renewable. Of that seven percent, hydropower and biomass make up the vast majority. Wind and solar are barely on the map.

The percentages in the previous paragraph change very slowly, because very few revolutionary things happen in our pattern of consumption. Still, there was a time when 100 percent of our energy came from renewable sources. It took early settlers a long time to find coal deposits. Firewood, tallow candles, animal labor, a small amount of work from windmills and hydro-driven machinery, and whale oil were the early energy sources.

When people speak of renewable energy, they usually talk about firewood, wind, direct solar, corn ethanol, sugar ethanol, or biodiesel. Every one of those sources is ultimately due to sunlight. Ocean waves are due to winds, so they owe their origin to the sun. Hydropower is also due to solar-caused evaporation. In fact, the only non-solar energy "renewable" sources of note are geothermal energy and tidal energy, and they are responsible for a negligible amount of our energy. In other words, the term *renewable energy*, in most people's minds is almost indistinguishable from the broadly defined term *solar energy*.

We understand the physics of all of those sources, but all too often we hear reference to "wind, solar, and *other* renewable energy." Trying to find out just what is meant by that unspecified *other* is about like trying to nail a custard pie to the wall. If somebody has a source of energy that is *better* than wind and solar, it should be first on the list. If that source of energy is not as good as wind and solar, then we may safely ignore it until wind and solar become significant.

There is a worldwide political effort, based on putative global warming, to reduce our emissions of carbon dioxide (CO_2) by over 80 percent by 2050; indeed, a bill presently before Congress would mandate an 83-percent-below-1990 reduction in CO_2 emissions by 2050. Since combustion of coal, oil, and natural gas produces CO_2, this would require a massive alteration of energy sources and uses, and in a very short time. We

---

[1] Data in this book mostly refer to the United States. Expressions like "we use" and "our energy" thus refer to the US. Worldwide data are explicitly noted.

will not discuss the climate issue[2] further in this book; suffice it to say that the political effort has enormous financial backing, and that some factions of society are hell-bent on accomplishing the change. This political pressure has resulted in mandates in many states for utilities to get some large fraction (often 20 percent) of their electrical energy from renewable sources by (say) 2020.

Obviously, we use a lot more energy than the Pilgrims did. Mostly, the increase is due to our increased population, although some is due to our use of energy in transportation, lighting, central heating, air conditioning, running television sets and computers, and all other modern conveniences.

We hear from many voices that the US has to be "weaned off" our "addiction to imported oil." These loaded terms are very misleading. Energy is essential to everything; we are no more addicted to energy than we are addicted to the necessity for food. And why do they say we are "addicted to *foreign* oil," rather than just to oil?

A baby weaned off mother's milk is not left to starve. If we are "weaned off" oil, what energy source will replace it? Renewable energy, perhaps, but precisely how might wind turbines in Kansas, ocean-wave machines on our coasts, or solar panels in the desert Southwest enable us to fly from Chicago to Boston? There is no way to avoid discussing both the broad picture and the gritty details.

In Chapter 2, we will be discussing questions that should come to the minds of people who give some thought to renewable energy sources in general, and solar energy in particular. All of those questions arise from general background knowledge.

We can go only so far in discussing energy without bringing in numbers. In order to understand the role of renewable energy in the US or in the world, we need to know how much energy is used for what applications, and we need to understand the renewable sources *quantitatively*. And when we do have the numbers, we must make sure that they can be legitimately and easily compared. That is, we must all speak the same language.

In this regard, we note that there is not one equation for wind-turbine power for Republicans and another for Democrats. There is not a liberal version or a conservative version. There is not a version for Libertarians or one for tyrants. There is not one for the wealthy and one for the impoverished; one for religious fanatics, one for atheists. The beauty of science is that it pays heed to nobody's desires or beliefs.

Chapters 1 through 7 contain background information. Chapters 8 and 9 deal with hydropower and wind power respectively. These forms of

---

[2] See Howard C. Hayden, *A Primer on CO$_2$ and Climate*, (Vales Lake Publishing, LLC at www.valeslake.com)

energy generation are due to *mechanical* energy, the tendency of water to run downhill and the kinetic energy of the wind. As wind is the fastest growing energy source, it has the longest chapter. Chapters 10 through 14 deal with heat. Sometimes the heat is used directly, and sometimes it is used to produce mechanical or electrical energy. Nuclear energy is considered as a heat source, because the primary usefulness of reactors is that they produce heat. Biomass is used as a heat source, such as when we burn wood, but the reason for existence of biomass is that chlorophyll absorbs light. Chapter 14 may be regarded as a transition to the study of light. Chapter 15 is about converting sunlight directly to electricity using photovoltaic (PV) cells.

In Chapter 16, we delve into miscellaneous non-solar sources, like geothermal energy, tides, and waves. They play a very limited role in the overall energy picture. Chapter 17 discusses subsidies and Chapter 18 provides a summary. There are two appendices.

Chapter 2   Questions for Inquiring Minds

There seems to be no shortage of enthusiasm for renewable energy. In this chapter, we consider a number of questions that must occur to inquiring minds.

For one, everybody realizes that man has inhabited the earth for a long time, and has used solar energy for millennia. If sunlight is abundant and easy to use, one may ask, why doesn't everybody simply use it, putting Exxon and the utilities out of business? Why *has* it diminished in importance from 100% down to about 7% in the US?

Questions about Home Heating

There is an abundance of books, newspaper articles, and magazine articles about using solar energy to heat homes. The style of writing varies from one to the other, but the rules for accomplishing the task do not. The rules immediately induce questions about solar energy generally.
The most important rule is

Rule #1: Insulate your house so well that *even* solar energy can heat it.

The rule is never stated this way, but *every* article on the subject of solar heating emphasizes how well a house must be insulated. A well insulated house is much more comfortable than a drafty one, and it will cost less to heat and / or to air-condition. Therein lie two excellent reasons to insulate well. However, you *must* insulate your house extremely well if you intend to use solar energy to heat the house.

Would that advice be offered if solar energy were a strong source, such as a nuke in the basement?

Rule #2: Install a heat collector as large as the roof.

The best candidates for solar-heated homes are those with large roof areas that face south. No expert says, "put in enough collectors to cover 10% of the roof." You have to cover *most* of the (south-facing) roof; the more the better.

Again, would that be necessary if solar energy were a strong source of heat?

A friend had a modest house built about 20 years ago and had a solar heat collector installed. Being young and naïve, he followed the (non-expert) builder's advice and had only one collector installed, which covers only about 20% of the south-facing part of his roof. Later, he criticized the builder for selling him only one, because—nice as it is—it simply doesn't provide enough heat.

Still, despite his desire to have more solar heat, the friend has not installed more collectors. Why is his professor's salary inadequate for him to afford a retrofit?

Rule #3: Install a *real* heating system as a backup.

Because the sun does not always shine, and because the weather may be too cold, it is always necessary to have a backup system for the solar system.

My daughter met a couple at a bed & breakfast in northern Vermont last winter. When she asked them where they were from, they cheerily replied, "Oh, we live in town." So why did they wind up staying at the B&B overnight? They lived off the grid [burning wood for heat] and had just returned from a week-long vacation. They knew it would take at least a day for their house to heat up to a comfortable temperature, so they decided to pay for ["thought they would enjoy"] the comforts of heat and a home-cooked breakfast provided by someone who is on the grid.

Would not *all* solar systems—for heat or otherwise—similarly require backup systems?

Rule #4: Install a storage system if you intend to have solar energy supply most of the heat.

A solar system obviously cannot supply heat when the sun is not shining — well more than half of the time in winter—or when the sun's rays are not directly falling on the collection system. There must be a storage/retrieval system if plans call for any solar heat to be delivered at such times.

Would not all solar systems require storage systems?

Would not all solar systems have to be overbuilt to "stock up" while the sun was shining?

How could you store high-temperature heat that might be needed for smelting iron, for example?

Questions about the Impact

Often, people speak of solar energy only in reference to home heating. Indeed, that is one of the best uses for solar energy. But society uses energy for other purposes as well. Suppose we were to pull out our magic wands and use solar energy for *all* of our space heat and hot water, both for homes and commercial establishments. How would that affect the total energy picture?

The inquisitive individual would know that domestic space and water heating would only be part of the total energy picture. Where would the energy come from for transportation, manufacturing, farming, refrigeration, air conditioning, and pumping the water that gets heated by the domestic solar water heaters? What about electricity for lighting, communications, and medical equipment?

Questions about Nighttime and Weather

Society uses energy around the clock, all seasons of the year, in good weather and in bad. It must therefore occur to rational people to ask: How do we use solar energy when the sun is not shining? Is *this* the reason we don't use it?

For only the cost of a lot of solar collectors and the necessary wiring, you can read by bright electric lights when the sun is shining. To run the same lights at night involves a few additions to the simple solar system. An inquisitive person might wonder how solar energy can be used when the sun is not shining, either because it is night or because the weather is overcast.

The inquisitive reader must wonder how large a bank of backup batteries would have to be to supply backup power for such energy intensive devices as clothes dryers. How rapidly can they be recharged? How big must the solar-cell array be to gather enough energy during a short day of winter sunlight to charge batteries enough to last for many cloudy days and nights? How much do the batteries cost, and how many must be used? How long might they last before they need to be replaced? What is the environmental impact of battery disposal/recycling?

Of course, a solar system can be built purely as a supplemental system without a backup solar system. But there is a backup system nevertheless, namely, the energy distribution we already have in place.

Questions about US and International Politics

A reasonable question, then, is this. During night or inclement weather, why not receive energy from another place in the world where the sun is shining? For example, when it is nighttime in both New York City and the Sonoran Desert in Arizona, how could we get energy from (say) the Saudi Arabian Desert?

And are we sure that we want to go that route? Wasn't there something about dependence upon the energy sources in the Middle East?

Questions about Seasonal Variations

The problems of winter must surely be triply, possibly quadruply bad, one must think. (A) The days are shorter; (B) the nights are longer; (C) the weather is colder; and (D) sunlight somehow doesn't feel as intense. How large must a solar collector be to gather light from the sun that is low in the sky to collect energy to get through long cold nights? Is there any way to use the summer sun to provide winter heat and winter electricity? And, if so, why isn't such a system available?

Questions Blowing in the Wind

Wind is yet another form of solar energy with which humanity has had long experience. The newspapers now carry frequent stories about wind farms that are being built around the country. Did we give a Wind Depletion Allowance to Exxon?

Why not put wind turbines on buildings in The Windy City? Is there some good reason why it hasn't been done?

Farmers are struggling to make ends meet (so what's new?). Can they make a better living selling electricity from wind turbines?

Questions about Hydropower

Especially in New England, our forefathers ran factories and fabric mills on hydropower, another manifestation of solar energy. Might there be some reason that hydropower has diminished in importance? (Hint: Do you have a waterfall in your backyard?)

Hydropower can be used to heat water for coffee. That is, descending water is the source of energy that raises the temperature of the water. But we know that water falling over a waterfall doesn't boil when it hits the ground. Doesn't this suggest that a lot of water has to go through a hydropower station to boil a little water?

Questions about the Oceans

The inquisitive reader is aware that the world uses very little energy obtained from ocean waves and tides, but also knows that engineers and entrepreneurs are fully aware of that energy. Are we avoiding the ocean's energy because Big Oil has bought the seashores, perhaps?

Doubtful.

Questions about Firewood

Firewood obviously had a running start, yet all biomass combined provides less than 3.2% of our energy [see Table A11] in the US, and most of that is used for heating. According to *Split Wood Not Atoms* bumper stickers, *some* people are using firewood, but the usage is not terribly widespread. *You,* dear reader, may not be using firewood. Are we to believe that *you* have sold out to Big Oil?

Paper comes from wood. Is anybody suggesting that there is more energy in scrap paper than there was in the wood from which it came?

And what about the frequent news reports about the disappearance of forests? Does this news imply that forests do not renew themselves fast enough to keep up? And why is it that when city dwellers cut down trees they must pay to have the valuable firewood hauled off their property?

Questions about Geography

We have all seen people put their finger on a map of the Desert Southwest of the US and sagely tell us that some small part of that territory "could" supply the US with enough solar energy for everything we do.

Just suppose, for the sake of argument, that this optimistic desert picture were true. How would the energy be transported to where it is used?

We have ways of transporting fuels and electricity, of course, that are in common use. We use supertankers (which don't float very well in the desert), pipelines, railroads, highways with tanker trucks, and high-voltage transmission lines. Typically, a large power station sends its power out on HV transmission lines in several different directions, each delivering about 250 MWe to 300 MWe of electrical power. The US uses as much electricity as the output of about 440 such power stations, on the average, not counting peak demand. There are actually over 9,000 individual power generators at about 2,000 different power stations.

Would society really tolerate a distribution system that brought all of our energy from the desert? (Hint: When was the last time they put a pipeline through *your* neighborhood?)

The sunniest countries lie in the tropics. Those countries could presumably be able to export solar energy to the US and Europe and make a handsome profit for themselves. But the astute individual knows that the US does not import solar energy from Ethiopia, Kenya, Sudan, Sumatra, or northern Australia. Moreover, the people in those places do not provide their own energy from sunbeams. How, one must ask, is northern Minnesota supposed to be able to do what can't be done in Peru?

Questions about Science and Engineering

Many people evidently see renewable energy *only* as a political or economic question. Some imagine, perhaps, that we simply lack the political will to make solar energy happen. Some others think that if we would just throw some money at the problem, we'd become a solar nation. There is an oft-repeated adage that if we would give Exxon a solar-depletion allowance, we'd be using solar energy tomorrow.

However, renewable energy is—first and foremost—a topic of science and engineering. It is worth exploring how renewable energy actually works in all of its various manifestations. The subsequent chapters deal with those questions.

Chapter 3   Rudiments of Energy

Whenever we bend something, shape something, heat something, cool something, move something, cut something—in short, do anything to anything—we use energy. Eighty-five percent of our energy comes from three fuels: coal, oil, and natural gas.

Irish Slave Labor

I heard snatches of an interview on National Public Radio on 9/30/02 with an Irish woman who wrote a book about the exploitation of poor Irish girls doing laundry in Irish convents. Basically slaves in the early part of the 20th century, they led a miserable existence.

Unfortunately, I didn't hear all of the interview, but I did hear the end. The author said that the labor unions were not interested in the girls' plight; the girls were of lower classes. Nor did the Church, which was the wealthiest institution in the world, take any interest. The author said that, in her view, *the only thing that ended the practice was the invention of the washing machine.*

Energy Conversion

There is a fundamental law of physics that is taught way back in grade school or middle school science. It is called *The Law of Conservation of Energy*, and also called *The First Law of Thermodynamics*. Energy may be converted from one form to another, but can neither be created nor destroyed.

When we "use" energy, we *convert* energy. For example, the fire under a skillet converts chemical energy into heat energy. Our automobile engines convert chemical energy into heat, thence to mechanical energy. Generators convert mechanical energy into electrical energy. Overall, the total amount of energy remains the same when we "use" energy. There is so much chemical energy in a kilogram of coal, and no more.

You may be aware of a modification of this law, namely that mass can be converted to energy, as is done regularly in nuclear plants. In fact, the energy released by converting a mere kilogram (2.2 pounds) of mass is sufficient to provide all of the electricity used for all purposes in city of about 700,000 for an entire year. For our purposes, we will simply regard mass as a form of energy that is usually extremely hard to release.

When we convert energy, however, not all of the energy we started with becomes useful energy. We only get some fraction of it. The useful fraction is called the *efficiency*.

Eventually, all of the energy we "use" becomes heat. An electric light of 8 percent luminous efficiency converts 92 percent of the energy fed into it into heat. But the visible light also becomes heat though being absorbed. Even light that shines out into outer space will *eventually* become heat.

With use, the *quality* of the energy decreases. The heat released by our electric appliances warms up the room somewhat, but the heat energy in the "hotter" room cannot be used to produce more electricity. Here, we are dealing with a very subtle law called *The Second Law of Thermodynamics*. This law begins with the simple premise that heat flows from hotter objects to colder ones, but evolves into profound statements pertaining to the efficiency of engines. There are many equivalent statements of this law, but the one that says the most with the least technical language is that randomness increases.

It is possible, very likely in fact, that most readers would be hard-put to define exactly what energy is. Rest assured that it was well after Sir Isaac Newton enunciated his three laws of motion and his law of gravitation that energy emerged as a distinct concept. Knowing that, it is far easier to explain examples of the conservation of energy than to give a rigorous definition of energy; we will defer that discussion to Appendix 1.

The First and Second Laws of Thermodynamics

There are several useful statements of the first and second laws of thermodynamics.

- The first law says that the most you can get is what you already have.
- The second law says you'll be lucky to break even.

Suppose we have an energy source such as a fuel and we want to convert that energy into another form, such as electrical energy. The first law says that we cannot get more electrical energy than is supplied by the fuel. The second law says that we will actually get less.

Another way of expressing these laws is this.

- You can convert mechanical (or other) energy to heat with 100 percent efficiency.
- You can convert heat to another form of energy, but the efficiency will be less than 100 percent.

If a moving block slides along a table, it eventually stops. At the beginning it has *kinetic energy*—energy due to its velocity—but friction converts that energy to heat energy (a tiny amount of it) until the block comes to rest and has no kinetic energy at all. Alas, that is the fate of all the energy we "generate" (convert from fuels, sunlight, winds, waves, tides…). One hundred percent of it eventually becomes heat energy.

Every day, whether we are aware of it or not, we convert heat to mechanical energy. Our automobiles are propelled by hot gas from combustion of gasoline that expands, pushing a piston that turns a crank. In electrical power stations, steam pushes pistons, or more commonly, rotates a shaft in a turbine. The hotter the steam is, the more efficient the engine. But the hotter the steam, the more corrosive it is, so there are limitations. Typically, the efficiency is somewhere between 25 percent and 40 percent. Automobiles have lower overall efficiency because they run at many speeds. Steam engines in base-load power plants run at a constant RPM under constant load, leading to higher efficiency.

Efficiency

The term *efficiency* is a technical term with more than a single meaning in common parlance.

A useful way to think of efficiency is to regard is as useful output energy divided by the input energy. For a simple example, if we put 2000 units of energy into a steam engine and get 600 units of useful mechanical energy, the efficiency is $600 \div 2000$, which is 0.3, or 30 percent.

How should we define the efficiency of a furnace, where the purpose is to extract heat instead of work? It is the heat energy put into the house divided by the energy provided by the fuel. Notice that mechanical energy is not involved in this calculation.

This one is a bit trickier. What is the efficiency of an automobile? Start with the car in the driveway. Drive away, buy groceries, go to work, or do whatever you want to, then go back home and park in the driveway. The car has had no change of energy. It is not moving, and it is not elevated compared to the starting point, so it has no kinetic energy and no potential energy. Nonetheless, something useful came of it, though not necessarily in the form of energy. We cannot define efficiency in this case by dividing one quantity of energy by another. Consequently, there is a different term called *fuel efficiency* expressed in America as miles per gallon[3] of gasoline. (In Europe, it would be kilometers per liter.) In the rail and trucking industries, this kind of fuel efficiency is reckoned as the product of weight carried and the distance traveled (ton-miles, in the US) per unit of fuel consumed.

We begin to see complications when we talk about hybrid cars. But first, imagine having a battery-powered car that is charged from the power

---

[3] Note on units of measurement: We will use familiar English units from time to provide context for readers not familiar with metric units. However, we shall soon see the folly of using them.

line, and has no gasoline engine. It has extremely high *fuel* efficiency—infinite—if you define that as the distance traveled divided by the amount of gasoline used. But that figure is entirely misleading.

Similarly, a hybrid car that can have its battery charged by the power line will use only a trivial amount of gasoline if the trips are short and infrequent. It is easy to imagine going 1,000 miles on a single gallon of gasoline, simply because the battery is doing almost all of the work, and the energy has actually come from a power station. This is possible when trips are very short and there is plenty of time to recharge the batteries.

There are thousands of 18-wheelers on the nation's highways that have driven over a million miles without burning a drop of gasoline. That's a silly claim, because the 18-wheelers use diesel fuel. But occasionally we do see newspaper articles extolling somebody's "high-mileage" vehicle that runs on (say) biofuels mixed in with some gasoline. They refer only to the gasoline, but not to the other fuel.

As far as efficiency is concerned, we really care most about distance traveled (or weight times distance traveled) per unit of *energy*, whether that energy be from diesel fuel, gasoline, fuel at the power station, sunlight (via biofuels), wind energy (used for charging batteries.)

Efficiency should not be confused with effectiveness. It is effective, but not efficient, to put in a picture hanger by using a sledge hammer. The motor in a household fan is efficient, but it would be very ineffective at lifting an elevator up the Empire State Building. Effectiveness has to do with getting a job done. Efficiency has to do with accomplishing the task with the least possible energy.

Power

Power is another term that has a well-defined technical meaning and several ill-defined meanings in common parlance. Electrical power is only one kind of power. It takes power to propel your car. In the US, we commonly refer to the former in watts and the latter in horsepower. But in science, both are power and only one unit of measurement is needed. We use the watt.

Energy is not power and power is not energy.

Let us begin with something simple. Suppose we have a cup of gasoline. We can burn up that gasoline very slowly or we can burn it up in a hurry, possibly even in an explosion. In both cases, the same amount of energy is released, because that cup of gasoline has just so much energy, no more, no less. When the fuel is burned slowly, that's low power. When it is burned rapidly, that's high power.

For a very dramatic example, consider the electrical energy from a single large coal-fired power plant operating for one half of a day. The energy is used for heating, refrigeration, lighting, manufacturing, and many other useful ventures. But if that amount of energy were expended in about a microsecond, it would be an explosion like that of the atomic bombs that befell Hiroshima and Nagasaki. That's extremely high *power*.

In all cases to which the term *power* applies, energy is being converted from one form to another. The faster the energy is converted, the higher the power.

Technically, then, *power = energy converted ÷ the time interval*.

Alternatively, *energy converted = power × the time interval*.

The Utility Bill

When you send a check to the utility, it covers two things. One is a fixed monthly cost covering equipment, maintenance, and personnel. The further cost is for producing the electrical *energy* you use. The energy is measured in kilowatt-hours (kWh)—the product of power in kilowatts times time in hours. It is useful to think that part of the bill as paying for the fuel used to produce the electricity you used.

It takes the same amount of energy to run a 100-watt light for 10 hours as to run a 1,000-watt (1-kilowatt) heater for one hour. That energy is 1,000 watt-hours (1 kWh), and the price for that is typically about ten cents. A typical household will use a few hundred kWh per month. Some homes use more, some less.

How much energy does it take to produce one kWh of energy? If the source of energy is heat, it takes about three kWh of heat to produce one kWh of electrical energy. If the electricity comes from a hydroelectric power station, it takes about 1.2 kWh of mechanical energy to get that much electrical energy. When a wind turbine draws kinetic energy from the moving air, it typically saps about 40% of the energy of the intercepted air.

Before long, we will introduce a different unit of energy, the *joule*. It may be an unfamiliar unit, but using it makes calculations much simpler.

With that as a basis, think of the speedometer in your car. The speedometer part tells how fast you are going, and the odometer tells how far the car has traveled. Nobody ever gets confused between the two concepts. Speed is not distance, and distance is not speed.

The meter that tells of your electrical usage is similar, having an indicator for power (the spin rate of the disk) and a different one (a digital readout) for energy consumed. See Fig. 1. When we are billed for electrical energy used, the utility subtracts the last month's kWh reading from this month's to see how much energy we used during the month.

Generally speaking, however, we don't have meters that tell us *directly* how much power we are using, or how much energy we have used.

A meter outside the house tells us how much natural gas we have used (totally); again, the utility must subtract readings to find the month's consumption. The reading is not in energy units, but rather in quantity of natural gas. The amount of energy must be calculated from the amount of gas.

Similarly, when a power station burns coal, they operators keep track of how much coal the plant has burned, and can calculate the amount of energy consumed.

Figure 1: A kilowatt-hour meter.

Chapter 4   US Energy History

In the colonial days of the US, the primary sources of energy were firewood and coal. There were some waterwheels used for running thread mills and there were draft animals. But the best records were kept for firewood and coal consumption. Because it was more widely available, firewood remained the dominant fuel.

American forests were the salvation of the British Navy. Deforestation in England, for firewood and shipbuilding, had gone so far that by 1662 the commissioners of the British Navy asked the nation's scientists for help in finding remedies. Britain then switched to coal for all heating requirements, but that didn't help with shipbuilding. That was where American forests came to the rescue, and that provided the main reason for colonization. By the time of the American Revolution, about one-third of British shipping was due to colonial construction.

The British also established an iron industry in America. That was, in fact, the reason for Sir Walter Raleigh's expedition in 1585. By the 1607 founding of Virginia, there were already one furnace and two forges in Falling Creek, 66 miles above Jamestown.

Early on, people used tallow for candles, but the wealthier people preferred whale-oil lamps, which burned cleaner. As the whales became scarcer, the price of whale oil rose about 6-fold in the ten years prior to 1832. Camphene (derived from vegetable oils), lard oil, and kerosene (made from coal) were the substitutes, but were soon pushed out of the market by crude oil (a better source of kerosene). By 1850 (see Fig. 2) coal was supplying about 10 percent of the nation's energy. The use of wood leveled off and then decreased somewhat. By 1900, coal was by far the dominant fuel, supplying about 70% of the energy. By the present date, coal's contribution to the overall energy supply is 22%, although it supplies 51% of our electricity.

Overall, the energy consumption in the US (2008) is 105,000,000,000,000,000,000 joules, variously written as 105 exajoules, 105×10^{18} J, and 105 EJ. (See Watts and Joules, p. 33 and Appendix A.)

The US annual consumption of energy (2008) is 105 EJ.

That's 105,000,000,000,000,000,000 joules

Annual US Energy Consumption 1635-2007

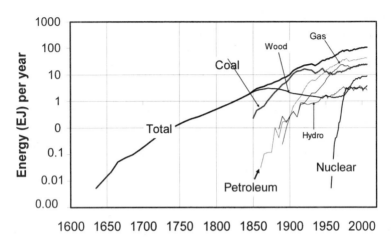

Figure 2: Energy consumption since 1635, by source.

Early on, firewood was the predominant energy source. By about 1850, coal was supplying about 10% of our energy and by 1900 was supplying about 70%. Since that time, petroleum, natural gas, hydropower, and nuclear power have been added to the mix. Notice that the energy scale is logarithmic: each grid line represents 10 × the energy of the next-lower grid line. The unit is the exajoule (EJ), representing 10^{18} joules.

Our present energy sources are shown in Figure 3. Petroleum (40%), natural gas (23%) and coal (22%) provide us with 85% of our present energy. "Renewable energy sources" (wood, waste, biofuels, hydro, wind and solar) combine to provide only 6.83% of our energy.

US Energy Sources 2007

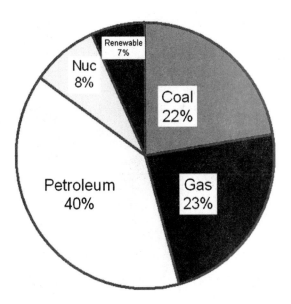

Figure 3: Sources of the energy consumed in the US in 2007.

Eighty-five percent of US energy comes from coal, oil, and natural gas. Renewable energy sources (6.83%, here rounded to 7% of the total) include wood, waste, bio-fuels, hydro, wind and solar.

A further breakdown of Fig. 3 is shown in Fig. 4, which shows only the contribution from renewable energy sources. Together, they supply 6.83% of US energy. The greatest non-nuclear renewable contributions are from hydro (36% of the renewable energy) and biological liquids (15%) and wood (32%), combining for 83% of US renewable energy sources.

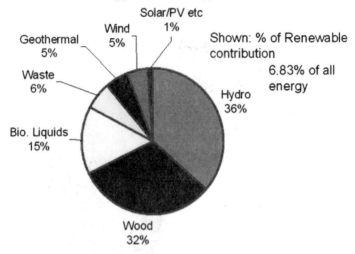

Figure 4: Contributions from sources of renewable energy.

Combined, they account for 6.83% of US total energy. Note that the largest contributions come from the venerable sources, hydro (36%) and wood (32%). Biological liquids (corn ethanol and biodiesel) and wood are all "biomass", and they combine to give 47% of the renewable energy, and with hydropower add up to 83% of US renewable energy. Much of the municipal waste is also biological. Wind contributes 5% of the renewable energy, or 0.31% of US total energy. Solar contributes 0.08% of US energy.

How We Use Energy

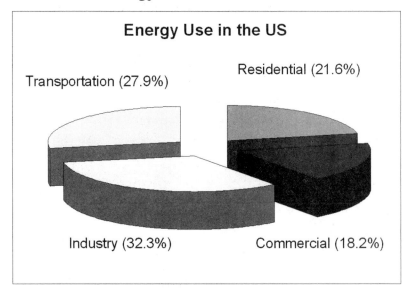

Figure 5: Energy use in the US. [Data from *Annual Energy Review*.].

There are about 100 million housing units in the US. Some 50 million homes are now heated by natural gas and 30 million are heated by electricity, as shown in Fig. 6. Fuel oil heats another 10 million.

The transportation, industrial, and residential/commercial sectors consume approximately equal amounts of energy, as shown in Fig. 5. Of course, transportation is powered almost exclusively by petroleum. Not shown in Fig. 5 is the electrical industry, because it is a pass-through technology. Electricity is not a source of energy, but only a transmitter of energy. The electrical industry uses 41% of the primary energy to produce the electricity, which is then sold to residential, commercial, and industrial customers. Despite the existence of subways and city commuter railroads, extremely little electricity goes into transportation.

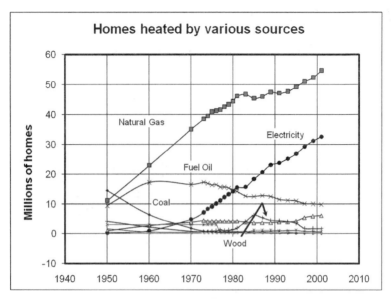

Figure 6: The number of homes heated by various methods, 1950–1997.

During the half-century shown, the number of homes heated by natural gas has steadily increased from 10 million to 50 million, while those heated by coal have decreased from 14.5 million to 180,000. Nearly 30 million homes are now heated by electricity. The renewable contributions are shown in Fig. 7 on a much-expanded scale.

Some homes are also heated by alternative sources, as shown by the lower curves in Fig. 6 and the four curves in Fig. 7. Following the oil embargoes of the 1970s, there was a big push to heat homes with firewood. Of course, that requires either a woodstove or a fireplace, neither of which was particularly common in the 1970s. As factories started churning out woodstoves, firewood heated more homes, reaching a peak of 6.3 million homes in the mid-80s. The subsequent decrease to fewer than 2 million homes heated by firewood was due to both the low cost of fossil fuels and the hard work associated with feeding a woodstove. Notice in Fig. 7 that the number of homes with no heat source at all exceeds the number of solar-heated homes. In 2007, there were 24 times as many homes with no heat source as there were with solar heat.

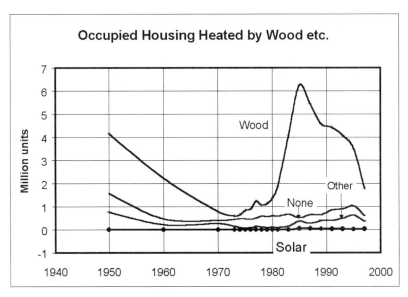

Figure 7: Data from Fig. 10, showing only homes heated by wood, nothing at all, other, and solar.

The large increase in wood-heated homes just after 1980 undoubtedly came as a result of the oil embargoes of the 1970s; the *de*crease after 1985 was undoubtedly caused by the realization that feeding a woodstove involves a lot of hard work. Despite the articles in Sunday supplements, solar homes are few and far between. A mere 0.02% of all US homes—one home out of every 5000 in 2007—are heated by solar collectors.

Energy History from 1800 to the Present

Let us begin our energy history with an oft-noted but misleading fact: The US uses a lot more energy in a year than we did in the past. Everybody "knows" this, because we have automobiles, trucks, railroads, airplanes, electric lights, household appliances, TVs, radios, cellular phones, huge factories, and skyscrapers that our ancestors did not have. Considering all energy sources now and then, the US used about two-hundred-seven (207) times as much energy in 2002 as the US did in 1800.[4]

But before you run off to destroy your family car, have another look. In 1800, the population was only 5.3 million people, including Thomas

---

[4] Energy data for early years from EIA *Annual Energy Review 2008*, Appendix E.

Paine, John Adams, and Thomas Jefferson; by 1850 it had more than quadrupled to 23 million. The US population is now 304 million, some 57 times as large as in 1800 and 13 times as many as in 1850.

Obviously we use a whole lot more energy now than our forebears did. What is not so obvious is that the lion's share of the increase is due to the population increase, even though we drive cars, have well-heated homes, use air conditioning in the summer, ship refrigerated food halfway across the continent, have a ready supply of cheap consumer goods, and have all the conveniences brought to us by electricity.

That is, the great majority of our increase in energy consumption is due to the increase in population; a much smaller effect is due to the amount of energy each person uses. Figure 8 shows the per-capita rate of energy consumption in the US since 1850, expressed in kW_t (kilowatts [thermal]) per person.[5]

The pre-1850 era was characterized by relatively constant consumption from the predominant energy source in use, firewood. Coal, used primarily for smelting, took on wider use as fuel for railroads, and took on other roles as well. After 1850, the use of coal and wood both increased, but the use of wood declined after about 1880 (See Fig. 2). Coal became the dominant energy source after about 1880, and remained so until the petroleum era. From the pre-depression era until the post-WW-II era, *per-capita* consumption was relatively constant at about 6.4 kW_t per person. The post-war industrial boom saw an increase to about 11.5 kW_t per person, a value that has changed little in the last three decades.

These energy figures do not account for energy used in manufacturing goods that we import, but do include energy used in export items. It is unlikely that the *net* energy is more than 10% of our overall energy consumption.

---

[5] Example: in 1950, the US population was 151 million, and the energy consumption during that year was 34.64 quadrillion BTU. This is equivalent to 7666 watts [thermal] per person. (The conversions will be discussed in Chapter 5 and in Appendix A.)

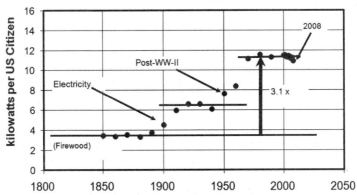

Figure 8: The average energy consumption rate for the US on a per-capita basis.

The average consumption was about 3.7 kW_t (kilowatts, thermal) per person until the 1890s when electricity and widespread rail traffic increased consumption to around 6.4 kW_t/person. Since the first OPEC embargo of 1973, per-capita consumption has been nearly constant at about 11.5 kW_t/person.

To gain a little perspective on these numbers, the pre-1850 value corresponds to thirty-five 100-watt bulbs running continuously for every man, woman, and child in the US. The present value corresponds to one-hundred-fifteen 100-watt bulbs continuously burning for everybody in the US.

Human food consumption (at 2050 food calories per day) is equivalent to 100 watts [thermal] per person. This figure is routinely used in the heating & air conditioning trade to account for the heating of the room by its occupants (in an auditorium, for example). An athlete in excellent shape, but given a more substantial diet, can actually perform work at the rate of about 100 watts. If he works for ten hours, he has done one kilowatt-hour of work. If he is paid $6.00 per hour, the kilowatt-hour of work comes at a cost of $60. The utilities that everybody likes to complain about charge about a dime for the same amount of energy.

The average per-capita US energy consumption rate in 2008 of 10.9 kW_t corresponds to the work of 109 athletic servants working for each of us around the clock. Readily available energy puts slave-owners out of business.

Efficiency

Efficiency in Households

The energy used by a typical US household currently amounts to about 3,200 joules for every second of the year. In other words, the average power consumption in US households is about 3,200 watts [thermal].[6] This figure has declined a bit from a high in 1970, but has held pretty steady since about 1980.

By comparison, homes in the early 1800s used much more power, mostly for heating. After all, their per-capita consumption was 3500 (thermal) watts (Fig. 4), and families were large. We can make a crude estimate. Assuming that half the energy of the society was used in homes and that the average family had six persons, the family home would have consumed about 10,000 watts,[7] mostly as heat from firewood. The houses of the era were large and poorly insulated. Moreover, they mostly used fireplaces, which are not nearly as efficient as woodstoves.

Efficiency in Automobiles

The pre-war standard for US cars was 20 miles per gallon (8.4 km/liter). The post-war automobile era saw a dramatic decrease in fuel efficiency as designers added a host of energy-consuming features to automobiles. Mostly, however, the cars steadily grew in weight. Many were about as boxy as 30s-era cars, not having been designed for aerodynamic properties. However, the post-war cars were driven a lot faster. Wind resistance causes cars to gobble up fuel.

Following the Arab oil embargoes, cars actually began getting *poorer* mileage for a while, and the cause was pollution-control measures that were being required at the same time as the energy crisis was in progress. For a quick fix, engineers threw energy at the problem, so to speak, in order to clean the exhaust.

Hope was on the horizon. Japanese cars already met some important requirements for the American market. They were smaller and more aerodynamic, and they also burned fuel more efficiently.

The computer has greatly improved matters. In the first place, engineers use computers to design cars and test their performance without

---

[6] *Annual Energy Review 2008*: 95 million BTU/household/year
[7] Again, this is not electrical watts. It is the annual energy consumption in joules (almost entirely for heating) divided by the number of seconds in a year.

having to build them.   Secondly, on-board computers also improve the engine performance.   They control the fuel input, second by second, looking at the exhaust to assure that the fuel/air mixture is right.   They also control spark timing.   Moreover, electronic ignition systems have vastly superior performance and durability than the old Kettering ignition system that cars used for the better part of a century.

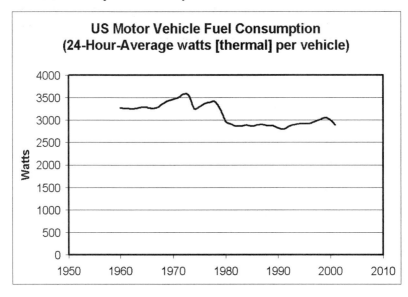

Figure 9:   The average power consumption of vehicles on American roads.

Includes motorcycles, buses, other 2-axle, 4-tire vehicles (including vans, minivans, pickup trucks, and sport-utility vehicles), single-unit trucks with six or more tires, and combination trucks.

The [thermal] power consumption of a car in motion is huge, typically in the range of 50,000 W_t (tiny cars) to 200,000 W_t (gas guzzlers) for cars going at highway speeds.   On an around-the-clock basis—total annual energy input divided by the number of seconds in a year—things are different.

Figure 9 shows that the average power consumption for all vehicles in the US, including everything from econo-boxes to tandem tractor-trailers. There is a slow downward trend in power consumption, as vehicles have become more fuel-efficient across the board.

Engine design is not the only consideration. Jack Stephens, Emeritus Professor of Civil Engineering at the University of Connecticut[8] was involved with a project a half-century ago to change the design of long-haul trucks to make them more aerodynamic. It was clear from the outset that better fuel economy could be achieved by merely changing the shape of the truck. The resistance to change came from truck drivers who thought there was something "sissy" about the new shape. After the price increases incurred as a result of the OPEC oil embargoes, they began to change their minds. The newer trucks are much sleeker and more fuel efficient.

---

[8] Private communication.

Chapter 5   Solar Energy in General

Sunlight is the source of energy for biomass, hydropower, wind power, wave power, and various forms of solar power generated in made-made devices. It is therefore appropriate to find a common language for use with all applications.

Sunlight is not a form of stored energy; rather, it is rather like a stream of energy with a rate of flow of so much energy coming our way per unit time. The sunlight that misses the earth is of no use to us. If we put up some kind of solar collector facing the sun, the only sunlight that matters is whatever falls within the boundary of our collector; specifically, it is the *area* that matters.

Accordingly, sunlight is best described as so much solar energy per unit time per unit area. This quantity is solar *intensity*, also known as *insolation*. (This term should not be confused with *insulation*.)

A device or system that captures the energy of sunlight can be described as catching a certain fraction—say, 5 percent or 60 percent—of that intensity, so its output can also be described in energy per unit area per unit time.

Numerous sets of units have been used in the past, such as calories per square centimeter per day, and tons of biomass per acre per year. While these units may be useful in certain circumstances, it becomes a chore to make the most fundamental decision in the entire field of measurement: *which is larger?* Let us show this conundrum by posing two problems, both of which use units that could represent solar intensity.

Solar energy problem 1. Which is the biggest?
- A. 11,700 calories per square centimeter during one month
- B. 254 BTU per square foot per minute
- C. 2 MWe generated per 130 acres of solar collector
- D. 1/2 cord of white oak per acre per year
- E. 397 Langleys per day

Solar energy problem 2. Which is the biggest?
- A. 100 W/m^2
- B. 673.2 W/m^2
- C. 23.7 W/m^2
- D. 200 W/m^2
- E. 0.001 W/m^2

In due time, and with a good table of conversion factors, one could figure out the answer to the first problem. The second problem is absolutely trivial for a child who understands numbers.

There are two lessons here. The first is that comparison of quantities is simple when the quantities are expressed in the same units. The second lesson is that the units should be universally recognized.

Let's pursue this matter. The following energy-related quantities are in common use. Units from the International System of Units are shown in italics:

Energy

> *Joule*, erg, BTU, calorie, kilocalorie, kilowatt-hour, gigawatt-year, horsepower-hour. Quasi-units: barrel of oil, ton of TNT, ton of coal, gallon of gasoline, cord of wood, ...

Time

> *Second*, minute, hour, day, week, month, year, century, ...

Area

> *Square meter,* square centimeter, square inch, square foot, acre, hectare, square mile, ...

Solar intensity can be expressed by any one of the energy choices (1) divided by any of the time choices (2) divided by any of the area choices (3), resulting in 728 different units. To make a single table to convert any one of these bizarre units directly to any other requires about a half-million conversion factors. And we're underestimating the situation, because people regularly use about 50 different energy units instead of the 13 shown.

Not every such unit, of course, is in common use; however; some are. Firewood production is reckoned in cords per acre per year. People will write that the US annual "energy" usage (yet another unit, but not a constant one) could be generated on 6000 square miles if solar collectors were 100% efficient (unit = US annual energy per year per 6000 square miles). Or, perhaps, a writer may say that if we devoted a mere 20,000 acres of desert to collecting solar energy, we could avoid using 50,000 gallons of petroleum per month in the summer (unit = gallons of petroleum per acre per month). Perhaps the writer is enthusiastic about solar energy, and perhaps he thinks solar energy is a joke. How can the reader gain any perspective when these numbers are so hard to compare?

The United States continues to use a variety of arcane units with equally arcane number systems. For example, we in the US still use base-16 arithmetic (16 ounces per pound, for example), and base-12 arithmetic (dozens of this, gross of that). But we also use mixed-base arithmetic (12 inches per foot, but inches divided into sixteenths) and base-60 hybrid systems (60 minutes per degree, 360 degrees per full circle). We use miles of 5280 feet length, and acres, defined so that there are exactly 640 acres per square mile.

A base-10 numerical system has the advantage that children learn to count on their fingers, but children could equally well learn to count the spaces between the fingers[9], as is the habit of cultures that have developed the base-8 system. Computers use the base-16 system, and its cousins, base-32 and base-64. The real advantage of the base-10 system is that nowadays everybody in the world uses it.

Similarly, we *could* redefine our time units so that there were (say) 10 billion seconds in a year or 100,000 seconds in a day, but through long usage, we are content with 60 seconds in a minute, 3600 seconds in an hour, and 86,400 seconds in a day. If every country had its own definitions, we would probably expend some effort to adopt a convenient universal time system. Instead, we use an inconvenient, *but universal* time system.

Historically, there have been thousands of units for measuring length volume, and weight, the units used in commerce. To simplify matters, as well as to keep people honest, the world has adopted universal units for length, volume, and weight, but also for everything else that we measure. If we use those units we are able to communicate with everybody everywhere.

The International System of Units (SI)

During the past century, the "metric" system has evolved from two different but related systems into one, the International System of Units (SI, standing for the French *Systéme Internationale*). The reason most often cited for going metric is that the English system is crazy with its threes, twelves, sixteens, and other numbers like 5280 and 1760. The SI system has tens.

The British have long since abandoned the English measurement system, as have the Canadians, the Australians and all other former British colonies. All scientists and engineers who received their degrees in the US since the 1960s have been trained in the SI system, but have often been

---

[9] You can place sticks between the fingers, making it easy to count relatively large numbers.

forced by circumstance to become mired in BTUs, feet, furlongs, horsepower-hours, acres, leagues, slugs, poundals, and ounces.

Yes, the British system is cumbersome, but that's just the beginning. A better reason to abandon it is that there are no units in the English system for electricity whatsoever.

The most important reason, however, is that we have to make comparisons. Can you tell at a glance whether 7 therms contains more or less energy than 364 gallons of gasoline? How many foot-pounds are there in a BTU? But any fool can tell that 15 of something is more than 10 of something when they are in the same units. That is the best reason for using the same units as everybody else in the world: *The International System of Units.*

You wouldn't know it from the way we behave, but the United States has adopted the metric system—many times. Here is a brief chronology of the metric system.

1585   Simon Stevin suggested that a decimal system should be used for weights and measures, and coinage. Moreover, he suggested measuring angles in a decimal system (as is now done in a number of countries where a right angle has 100 grads instead of 90 degrees).

1790   Thomas Jefferson recommended both a decimal currency and decimal measurement.

1792   The US Treasury produced the world's first decimal currency. (It only took until 2001 for the decimal system to hit the stock market.)

1821   John Quincy Adams wrote a report suggesting the adoption of the metric system. He concluded the report, however, with the recommendation "this may not be the right time to change." This excuse has been used repeatedly since then.

1866   The metric system was made legal (but not mandatory) in the United States by the Metric Act of 1866 (Public Law 39–183). (The English system has never been legalized.)

1875   The U.S. joined 17 nations to form the Treaty of Metre.

1889   The U.S. received a prototype meter and kilogram to be used as measurement standards. That is, we have a metal bar with two scratches that are exactly one meter apart. We also have a standard 1-kg weight[10]. [Nowadays, we define the meter in terms of the wavelength of light from certain atoms. The weight standard remains a certain 1-kg piece of metal.]

---

[10] In 1899, the kilogram was a unit of weight, not mass.

1893 The US officially adopted the prototype standards in lieu of its previous length and weight standards. It is of interest that there is no such thing as a standard bar for the inch, foot, or yard. Our English units are defined in terms of the metric standards. The inch is defined to be 2.54 cm (0.0254 m) *exactly*. Similarly, our standard pound is defined to be 1/2.205 of a kilogram *exactly*.

1975 The Metric Act was signed into law making metric the preferred system in the US, but it set no target dates.

1988 President Reagan signed a law making all new Federal projects metric, and required all federal agencies to be metric by the end of fiscal year 1992. (The Department of Energy routinely ignores the law.)

1991 President George H. W. Bush signed Executive Order 12770, directing all executive departments and federal agencies to implement the use of the metric system.

Watts and Joules

Non-technical people have little experience with the *SI* units for power and energy, but know of the watt through its association with electricity. The watt, however, is not inherently electrical.

The Energy Information Agency (part of the Department of Energy) uses a bizarre array of energy units in its ***Annual Energy Review,*** but that is still a small fraction of the fifty or so energy units in common use. So do the folks who assemble the ***Statistical Abstract of the United States.*** You need a calculator and a table of conversion factors just to read their tables and compare what's on one page with what's on another.

Never mind that the US government pays no attention to the US government; the international unit of energy is the *joule*.

The energy required to heat a cup of water by one degree Fahrenheit is about 1000 joules. A shot glass of gasoline will produce about two million joules of heat when burned.

Let us emphasize: The joule is the unit used for the quantity of energy. The watt is the unit for the rate of energy conversion (power). The relationship between the two is expressed as

A joule is a watt-second.

and

A watt is one joule per second

The term *watt-second* means a watt *times* a second. We multiply power in watts times time in seconds to get energy in joules.

The Underlying Simplicity

There is an underlying simplicity to solar energy. Regardless of whether we are talking about home heating, photovoltaics, biomass, arrays of mirrors, or thermal-gradient ponds, there is something universal to all: sunlight. We have but one sun, the same one our forefathers had. The sun is no different now than it has been for millennia, except for minor changes in output.

It is true that we now know more ways to use solar energy, and that we have even improved the efficiency of various traditional solar energy systems. But that doesn't make things complicated. A nineteenth-century physicist would not be amazed that we can convert sunlight to electricity, though he might wonder what we intended to do with the electricity. He already knew how to generate electricity with thermopiles. R. E. Day discovered the photovoltaic effect—producing electricity directly from sunlight—in selenium in 1878, four years before Edison's Pearl Street Station started producing power for New York City.

But the transcendent issue about solar energy is sunlight itself, not the technology about how it is used. Suppose that somebody invents a solar-powered device to do something we haven't even imagined yet. The device would be inherently limited by the energy it absorbed from the sun. Solar energy devices do not create energy; they merely transform—*some of*—the sunlight into other forms.

With few exceptions, solar-energy manifestations can all be expressed in the same units as those for solar intensity. For example, firewood production, often expressed in cords of wood per acre per year can be expressed in watts per square meter. Food production is often expressed either as tons of product per acre per year or as food calories per acre per year; obviously they can be expressed in watts per square meter. The advantage of doing so is that it allows us to compare—directly, without have to look things up in tables and do tedious calculations—the actual product with the solar cause.

A hydropower dam uses water that has been collected from a huge collection area; it can produce a given average power throughout the year. Hydropower, then, can also be expressed with the same concept, power per unit area.

A larger wind turbine can produce more power than a smaller one; however, larger wind turbines have to be spaced more widely. Here, too, the same comparisons can be made. A given land area can produce a given average year-round power. It is a simple matter to express the wind turbine farm's output in units of power per unit area, the very same unit as for solar intensity, or *insolation*.

Of course, man-made devices all have a given surface area that is made to face the sun (and occupy a certain area on the earth), and can produce a certain average power, be it thermal or electrical. Regardless, they can all be expressed in solar intensity units, power per unit area.

When all manifestations of solar energy are expressed in one standard set of units, everything becomes simple. Appendix A in this book contains factors for converting other units to SI units.

Bad Units Are One Cause of Disagreements

How can it be that some people are extremely enthusiastic about solar energy and others see little hope for it? After all, we have but one sun, and the energy it sends us has been well known and well understood for over a century. The world's present energy consumption is well known; no information is being kept secret from the public.

If the sun is to supply our energy, then the year-round average power consumption should equal the year-round average solar power production. One only needs to look at the numbers.

Unfortunately, the simplicity is usually obscured by a bizarre collection of parochial units. How many days must the sun shine on 274 acres of solar collector to produce the equivalent of 22 therms, of 886,000 BTU, or of 17 barrels of oil?

The lesson here is that we have to simplify our discussions of energy by using the one system of units understood by scientists and engineers all over the globe.

Simplicity Through Rational Units

The international system of units (SI, *Systeme Internationale*) uses base-10 arithmetic throughout, except for the historical units of time. In the SI system, the basic unit of length is the *meter* (not the centimeter, and not the millimeter, and not the kilometer), and the basic unit of time is the *second*.

Americans recognize the terms *watt* and *kilowatt-hour* because of their use in electricity. There is, however, nothing uniquely electrical about either one of the terms. It is perfectly acceptable to say that a moving car consumes fuel at the rate of 100,000 watts, even though electricity is not moving the car. The term *watt* is simply the SI unit for power—energy per unit time—regardless of the source of energy.

It is not always clear from context whether the term *watt* is being applied to electricity or to some other kind of power. Power plant engineers use *MWe* to refer to megawatts-electric, and *MWt* to refer to megawatts-thermal. A watt of sunlight has the same heating power as a watt of electricity—one joule of energy per second—but the solar watts are not electrical.

A 100-W lamp draws 100 watts of electrical power. If it runs for an hour, the amount of energy it has consumed is 100 watts times one hour, or 100 watt-hours. If it runs for 10 hours, then it uses 1000 watt-hours, or one *kilo*watt-hour. Your electricity bill is for the electrical energy (expressed in kilowatt-hours) used during the month.

However, neither the watt-hour (Wh) nor the kilowatt-hour (kWh) is the SI unit of energy, because the hour is not the standard unit of time. For better or for worse, the standard unit of time is the *second*, so the *standard unit of energy is the watt-second*, otherwise known as the *joule*. (Therefore, the kilowatt-hour is 1000 watts × 3600 seconds = 3,600,000 joules.)

Let us now revisit the problems with which we began this discussion. Solar intensity is in units of *power per unit area*, for which the SI units are *watts per square meter* (W/m²) and no other. When we use the SI unit, we are automatically in tune with all scientists and engineers everywhere. *By using one agreed-upon system we bypass all problems of the type in Solar Problem 1 on page 29.*

For sunlight, the "insolation" (solar intensity, aka solar flux) values are given in Table 1. The units are watts per horizontal surface of one square meter, except for the first entry, which is in units of watts per square meter positioned to face the sun.

Table 1: Solar Intensity Values

	Watts/m²
At earth's orbit (above atmosphere)	1367 [11]
At surface, noon, tropics, clear skies	950
Maximum conceivable 24-hour average, at equator, no clouds, at equinoxes	300
Albuquerque, New Mexico, yearly average	240
US, 48 states, around-the-year, around-the-clock average	200
Hartford, Connecticut yearly average	160

---

[11] http://rredc.nrel.gov/solar/#archived. The value accepted in the 1970s was 1353 W/m², about 1% lower than the currently accepted value.

The solar intensity in the US, averaged over all places and over every second of the year, night and day, summer and winter, is about 200 W/m^2. (See the reference in footnote 11 for city-by-city data.) The yearly average at Hartford, CT, is 20% lower than that value, and the value in Albuquerque, NM is 20% higher. In fact, the average solar intensity is within that ± 20% range throughout over two-thirds of the US.

US Energy from Solar?

The land area of the United States is about 8 trillion square meters—3.096 million square miles——not including Alaska and Hawaii. Suppose that all of that land could produce energy at the rate of x watts per square meter. How large would x have to be to produce the 105 EJ we use per year?

The answer is easy to figure out. Divide 105 × 10^{18} joules by the number of seconds in a year—3.16 × 10^7—to get 3.3 × 10^{12} watts. Divide that by the number of square meters, and the result is about 0.4 W/m^2. That is, if every square meter in the US could provide an average of 0.4 watts of thermal power, we could supply all of the energy used in the US continuously.

That number is small compared to the 200 W/m^2 of average solar intensity. Bear in mind, however, that sunlight is not the same as electricity or motive power.

Translating

Berman and O'Connor offer the following description of the LUZ International plant in the Mojave Desert:

> "The largest solar electric generating plant in the world is the 355-megawatt LUZ International 'solar-thermal' plant, located between Los Angeles and Las Vegas, which delivers its power to Southern California Edison. Not a photovoltaic plant, LUZ is a 100-acre field of parabolic [mirror] trough collectors in the Mojave Desert…"
>
> Berman & O'Connor (1996)

The LUZ plant produces 355 MWe of electricity in full sunlight, as we will discuss more thoroughly on page 125. The authors' implication is clear: 355 MWe of *electricity* is delivered to Southern California Edison. However, the intensity—355 MWe per 100 acres—amounts to 877 watts per square meter, just under the intensity of sunlight falling on a surface that directly faces the sun at high noon in the tropics. For the plant to deliver all the electricity claimed by Berman and O'Connor, it would have to be nearly

100% efficient, which it certainly is not. Had the authors used SI units, they would have been able to spot the error in an instant.

The Seasons

The sunlight striking the ground (a horizontal surface) is *much* less intense in winter than in summer. For example, at 40° north latitude (New York) less than half as much sunlight falls on a tennis court between 11:30 a.m. and 12:30 p.m. during the winter as it does during the same hour in the summer, given identical clear-sky conditions.

However for a surface that directly faces the sun, there is very little difference between the amount of sunlight striking the surface for the one-hour period around noon in the summer and the winter. In fact, the difference comes entirely from looking at the sun through more of the atmosphere. If you could look straight up to the sun, you would be looking through one thickness of atmosphere, but when you look at the winter sun, you look at it through the *slant height of the atmosphere.* There is some reduction of intensity, but not all that much at temperate or tropical latitudes.[12]

Figure 10 shows the solar intensity versus the angle of the sun as measured down from the zenith (the line pointing straight up at the location). The arrows in the figure refer to 40-degree latitude, approximately the latitude of New York, Indianapolis, Denver, and northern California. At noon on the summer solstice, the sun is 16.5° off the vertical. At noon on the equinoxes, approximately March 21 and September 21, the noon sun is 40° below the vertical, and at the winter solstice, the sun is 63.5° below the vertical. During the year, the intensity of sunlight at noon varies from a high of just under 950 W/m² to a low of about 750 W/m². That is, sunlight on a clear day in mid-December is only 21% less than it is in mid-June.

For the two solstices, however, the lengths of daytime are considerably different. Between sunrise and sunset in mid-June, there are 15 hours. In mid-December, the sunlight lasts a little less than 9½ hours. That is, there is 38% less time when the sun is shining.

There is a difference between the amount of the sunlight received on a horizontal surface and that received by a surface that is continually adjusted

---

[12] Aden E. Meinel and Marjorie P. Meinel, *Applied Solar Energy,* (Addison-Wesley Publishing Co., Reading, MA, 1976), give the following equation for determining the solar intensity for clear skies, given the angle z of the sun, as measured from the zenith: $I = I_0 e^{-c(\sec z)^s}$, where $c = 0.357$, $s = 0.678$, and I_0 is the solar intensity above the atmosphere.

so as to face the sun at all times. For example, recent several-year average data from Albuquerque (see footnote 11) show that the average solar intensity on a horizontal surface is 233 W/m², whereas the average solar intensity on a surface that follows the sun is 366 W/m².

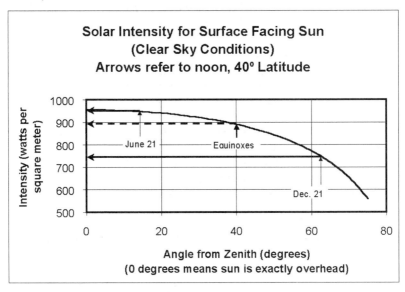

Figure 10: Solar intensity (W/m²) versus angle

The angle of the noon sun is measured from the zenith (directly overhead) for 40° latitude (Philadelphia, Salt Lake City), calculated from the equation in footnote 12. Notice that the vertical axis starts at 500 W/m², not zero. The intensity is 890 W/m² when the sun is 40° off the zenith, regardless of whether it is late in the day in summer or noon in mid-March.

For a single, sophisticated, two-axis tracking device, the higher intensity is more relevant. However, if one has an array of collectors in a field, the lower figure is the correct one to use for estimation. The reasons will be made explicit in the discussion of Solar Two on page 120.

Physical Laws

The laws of physics are not recipes. For example, all airplanes obey the laws of physics at all times, yet the very same laws do not tell anybody the best shape for a wing or the best design for an engine.

But physical laws do provide constraints. That is, they tell us what we *can't* do.

Perhaps nothing better illustrates these points than solar energy. The amount of light that comes to us from the sun is (within small variations) constant, the same year after year, century after century. In fact, enough light reaches the *upper* atmosphere every year to melt a layer of ice about 30 meters thick spread out over the entire earth. But when we write down a figure for that amount of sunlight, our ciphers do not tell us how to use all (or any part) of that energy. They do not tell us how to build solar water heaters, photovoltaic collectors, or solar-powered calculators. The fact that we understand how much solar energy impinges on the earth does not tell us how to design anything that will make use of it.

But that figure does provide a constraint: the earth cannot receive any more solar energy than the sun sends us. The constraint is just as true for a given parcel of land in a given time interval. The laws of science tell us that no solar collector—no matter how much research is done into improving efficiency—can collect more solar energy than is sent to the collector by the sun.

Let me emphasize this point. Science textbooks beginning at the lowest level instruct that energy can be neither created nor destroyed, although it can be converted from one form to another. The only solar energy that the collector (such as chlorophyll or a photocell) can convert is the energy that the collector absorbs. And all of that sunlight comes from our one and only sun.

There is more to this story. No device, either natural or man-made, converts *all* of the solar energy it absorbs into useful energy. Every solar collector of every kind merely converts *some of* the solar energy it receives into energy of another kind. For example, chlorophyll does not create energy, but converts *some of* the solar energy that strikes it into chemical energy.

Chapter 6   Conservation and Efficiency

All of the subsequent chapters in this book are about renewable energy in its various manifestations. Conservation and efficiency, the topics of this chapter, are *not* manifestations of renewable energy. Rather, they deal with how well we use energy.

It seems obvious that conservation and high efficiency are desirable goals; indeed there are people who dedicate their careers to improving both. But sometimes what seems obvious is not necessarily true.

Conservation

The term *conservation* has both a technical meaning and an everyday meaning. Unfortunately, the two meanings are somewhat contradictory.

To a physicist or engineer, the term *conserved* refers to physical quantities that can be neither created nor destroyed. Energy is one of these quantities, along with momentum, angular momentum, electric charge, and a few others.

In common parlance, *conservation* actually refers to things that are *not* conserved in the technical sense. If you drive your car less, you use less fuel. In the everyday sense, you have "conserved fuel." In truth, fuel is destroyed by burning; technically, the quantity of fuel is not conserved. Begging the forbearance of scientific colleagues, I will use the common parlance. I will also refer to fuel and energy *savings*.

That much said, it is understood by all that our fossil fuels are limited, and that we should not be wasteful.

Why bother saving energy?

Saving energy saves money, but is that all?

If the supply of a commodity is infinite, there is little point in saving it. As of press time, there is no known governmental program in Egypt to save sand, or in the Amazon to save water.

If you were given some annual allocation of, say, 500 liters of heating oil (and no firewood or other fuel) every year to get you through the winters in a northern climate, then you should insulate your house very well. You should also be very careful to keep the house just barely warm enough for mere survival so that you don't run out of oil before the winter is over.

Go back to the same picture, but with the following modification: you are given 500 liters of oil, and *that is all the energy you will ever get.* The 500 liters must last you and all of your descendants *forever.* You may figure out some scheme—using 100 liters per year, for example—that will maximize *your* life expectancy, but it is only a time-buying operation, and leaves nothing for your progeny.

Now look at the worldwide energy picture. In a given year, the US uses one-quarter of the energy consumed in the year, and the rest of the world uses three-quarters. Think of that as four logs on the fire, one labeled US.

Let us suppose that we want to do the right thing, which is to save energy. However, we will "take it to the max.". *We will cut our energy usage by 100%, and use no energy whatsoever.* We'll take that US log off the fire, and donate it to posterity. We'll store it in New York's Museum of Natural History so that visitors can see our energy supply along with the Hope Diamond, both of which are "saved" and neither of which is "used."

According to the commonly accepted scenario, the three logs remaining on the fire will soon be gone, perhaps in three decades, as is commonly assumed. Then the remaining log (retrieved from the museum) will be gone in less than one additional decade. The net effect of our Green zeal—aside from a few hundred million US deaths caused by lack of energy—is a few years of survival for the rest of the world.

And what great benefit will ensue if we would cut our energy consumption by only 10% instead of 100%? Less than a year of continued civilization, given the assumption that we'll otherwise run out of energy in three decades.

So, aside from the very legitimate purpose of saving money that might be used for other purposes, saving energy simply buys time—and not much of it—*if* we indeed would run out of fuels in the immediate future. That is, contrary to popular opinion, ***conservation of fossil fuels provides no guarantee that they will last very far into the future***.

Conservation does make sense when there is some continuing but *feeble* supply. That is the case with solar energy. The total amount of solar energy from all its forms combined—wind turbines, firewood, hydropower, direct sunbeams, and anything else you care to name—is so small that only extreme conservation measures gives solar energy a realistic chance of supplying our needs.

With abundant energy supplies—nuclear fission, and (if we can make it work) nuclear fusion—conservation may have its merits, but saving energy resources is not one of them.

Home Insulation

Our pioneering ancestors understood perfectly that well-insulated houses were easier to heat than poorly insulated ones. Unfortunately, they had few options. The best ones were tightly caulked log cabins, but they required a lot of wood.

Now we use stud walls that are usually insulated with fiberglass. This product was invented in the middle of the 20th Century. Styrofoam and its relatives came even later.

Heat loss depends upon the thermal resistance—the so-called *R*-value. (See Insulation and R-value on page 198 for details.) The important part is that the heat loss through a wall increases with increasing temperature difference between inside and outside, and with the area of the wall. The heat loss decreases as the wall thickness increases.

Insulation in Solar Homes

Heating bills in almost any home can be reduced by improving the insulation. Doubling the thermal resistance cuts the heat loss in half. Doubling it again can cut heat loss in half again. Some people go overboard in insulating homes, turning them into houses with walls as thick as those of a medieval castle, but insulated with fiberglass and Styrofoam instead of stone. A heavily insulated home requires much less heat in winter and much less cooling in summer.

There are often accounts in the Sunday supplements of new solar homes, complete with photographs and wondrous tales of lower heating bills. Usually, both reporter and homeowner alike attribute the improvement to sunlight. More correctly, most of the *improvement* comes from improved insulation. Most of the *expense* comes from installing solar collectors.

The advantages of good insulation are not limited to saving money. A well-insulated home is not drafty, nor does it have uncomfortable cold spots. For a solar home, superb insulation is an absolute necessity. Otherwise, solar energy doesn't have a chance to heat the home in any cold climate. The insulation is just as necessary in hot climates to reduce air conditioning bills.

Contrary to Popular Belief ...

There are two popular notions about conservation and efficiency that are manifestly incorrect. Let us address them.

Let us begin with a few assertions commonly made in the news media.
- Insulation is a good idea.
- Driving efficient vehicles is a good idea.
- Using efficient motors is a good idea.
- Turning off unnecessary lights is a good idea.
- In short, saving energy is a good idea.

What Conservation is NOT

That's all mother-and-apple-pie stuff that nobody disputes.   But it has become chic to add a totally false proclamation, namely, that conservation is a *source* of energy.   I would challenge anybody to demonstrate that assertion by locking himself or herself in a well-insulated empty room, and use every method of conservation, thereby to fill one shot-glass with gasoline.

Such nonsense is unfortunately rather widespread. By being efficient, we can use less energy for project *X*, and have more available for project *Y*; however, to regard conservation as a *source* of energy is merely to play with words.

There are many good arguments to be made for conservation, but its being a source of energy is not one of them.

> *Conservation is no more a source of energy*
> *than*
> *Dieting is a source of nutrition*

Hungry? Go diet!

What High Efficiency Will Not Do

It is "obvious" to the casual observer that if our machines were more efficient, we would use less energy; however, nothing could be further from the truth.

Imagine, as we discussed above, that our engines were the inefficient Newcomen engines of the mid-1700s, producing 5 joules of work for every 10,000 joules of input heat from coal. How much energy would all of the cars on the road be using today? Very little. Nobody could afford them. The cost of manufacture would be extremely high, and so would the cost of fuel.

The same phenomenon has been true of computers. When many kilowatts of input power to large mainframe computers of the 1960s produced results more slowly than today's handheld flea-power calculators, the total amount of energy used every year for calculating was utterly negligible in the US energy picture. Now that computing efficiency has become extremely efficient compared to that in the past, the major increase in demand for electric power has come from computer-related activities.

Peter Huber[13] comments,

"The U.S. today consumes 100 quadrillion BTU (quads) of thermal energy in a year. In 1950 the figure was 35 quads; in 1910, about 7 quads, not counting horses and other agricultural sources.

"The efficiency of energy consuming devices always rises, with or without new laws from Congress. Total consumption of primary fuels arises alongside. The historical facts are beyond dispute. When jet engines, steam power plants and car engines were much less efficient than they are today, they consumed much less total energy, too."

But the efficiency paradox is nothing new. In the 19th century, the efficiency of steam engines was steadily improving as a result of James Watt's steam engine. For a while, the consumption of coal decreased by as much as a third, but in the subsequent thirty-three-year period the consumption increased tenfold. An English economist, Stanley Jevons, commented on the paradox in 1865[14]:

"It is wholly a confusion of ideas to suppose that the economical use of fuel is equivalent to diminished consumption. The very contrary is the truth ... It is the very economy of its use

---

[13] Peter Huber, "The Efficiency Paradox," *Forbes*, p. 64, August 20, 2001.
[14] Thanks to J. C. Maxwell of New Galloway, Scotland, for furnishing me with this quotation from Jevons.

which leads to extensive consumption. It has been so in the past and it will be so in the future."

When we find ways to increase efficiency, we reduce our overall consumption, but only temporarily. We soon find ways to use energy that were previously too expensive. When our cars become more fuel-efficient, we drive more. When the Internet becomes faster, we send more information. When lighting becomes cheaper, we tend to light up the outdoors, much to the dismay of astronomers. When refrigeration becomes cheaper, we buy both a refrigerator and a freezer. When hot water is cheaper, we install hot tubs.

Summary

Conservation and efficiency have their merits, but the concepts are vastly over-rated. Even extreme conservation cannot guarantee the existence of a fuel in the future. The effect of increasing efficiency is not to decrease consumption, but paradoxically rather to increase consumption.

Chapter 7   Useful Classification Scheme

Although this book is entitled *A Primer on Renewable Energy*, there is no really meaningful distinction between renewable energy and non-renewable energy. The reason is that there is no such thing as infinitely renewable energy. The only really important distinction is that some sources of energy will last longer than others.

The concept of renewability is linked to one's concept of the future of humanity. If you believe, for example, that the earth is about to experience a collision with a huge asteroid that will destroy human life next week, be assured that we have enough energy to last that long. In that scenario, we are safe in saying that we have unlimited amounts of coal, oil, natural gas, whale oil, firewood, and all other kinds of energy you care to mention. Who cares if they're renewable?

If you believe that humanity needs enough energy to last until the sun turns into a Red Giant in a few billion years, then we need to consider energy in a whole different light.

Petroleum will not last *forever*, but neither will solar energy. The fate of the earth after the sun has turned into a Red Giant is only of academic interest, but the sun will not produce copious amounts of energy *forever*. For our purposes, that is more than enough time. If there is enough of a source to outlast humanity's time on Earth, then it may be regarded as "unlimited", whether it is "renewable" or not.

On the other hand, a renewable energy source may well have a limited rate of renewability. For one silly example, the grass in my yard does not grow fast enough to supply my house with heat through the winter. In other words, if a source is inherently inadequate, its renewability is irrelevant.

Another question is whether renewability is limited by our means to produce the energy. For example, if a dam fills up with silt so that it can't store water, the site can no longer produce hydropower. If so much heat is extracted from a geothermal source that it cools down too much, the site becomes worthless, even though the amount of geothermal heat *in principle* remains enormous. If we run out of fertilizers that are necessary to produce sugar cane in large quantity, it might not make sense to consider sugar cane as a renewable source of energy. If there had been a geothermal power source on the side of Mount St. Helens, it would now be worthless.

Should we consider energy sources as "renewable" if they are so long-lasting that they never run out? (Nuclear energy fits that category.) And if humanity somehow forgets the technology to use it, should *that* source of energy be considered either long-lasting or renewable? (Nuclear again.)

On a very short time scale, the concept of renewability encounters another problem. After the sun sets, solar-electric systems cease operation. No matter how well photovoltaic cells may provide electricity during the day, they don't work at night.   Shall we consider solar electricity "renewable" when it won't even last longer than a few hours?   Is wind energy "renewable" during the time that the air is idle?

Again, the point that matters is time. The important question is *How much energy* can we get *how fast, when* from *what sources*?

An Enumeration of Energy Sources

Energy comes in so many forms that we can actually classify them into categories.

The first distinction is between energy sources that are inherent in the earth, and those that are due to radiation from the sun. In the first category the best-known is the lode of coal, oil, and natural gas. There is also high temperature located deep beneath our feet and occasionally near the surface in volcanoes and hot springs. A more subtle energy form is in the tides, which are due to gravitational interactions with the moon and the sun. Mostly, tidal variations are very small, but there are places where the tidal range is large. Totally insignificant in this picture is the energy of cosmic rays and micro-meteorites that impinge on the earth. They may well affect *climate*, but, to put it mildly, there is no way to take advantage of that energy.

Light from the sun heats the earth and causes evaporation, thereby leading to wind, waves, and hydropower. We can capture the heat in numerous ways to heat homes and domestic water, and even to produce electricity.

But the light itself acts directly—not through heating—causing photosynthesis, producing plants that can be used for energy. As well, we can produce electricity directly from light using photovoltaic cells (PV cells).

In this chapter, we will list many sources of energy, whether they have any practical applications or not.

Terrestrial Energy

We presently get eighty-five percent of our energy from coal, oil, and natural gas, all of them obtained by mining and drilling into the earth. Arguments have raged for well over a century as to how much energy is down there somewhere waiting to be discovered, and we will not enter that fray in this book. Suffice it to say that the amount of energy in those fuels is limited.

The heat energy deep in the earth is not due to pressure, despite what may is said in some elementary science books. Pressure causes heating only when the volume of the pressurized material diminishes, when it is "squeezed down" so to speak. Indeed, in the nineteenth century, Lord Kelvin did a historic calculation based on the copious rate of heat flow out of the sun, relating it to compression from an initial radius extending all the way out to Earth's orbit. He supposedly proved that the sun, hence the earth, could not possibly be as old as the geologists had been proclaiming. Similarly, an earth that had such a hot interior simply could not result from compressing the earth to its present size if it were as old as the geologists claimed.

There was a Mexican stand-off between the physics and geology professions about the topic until the discovery of radiation by Becquerel in 1891. Suddenly there burst upon the scene a source of energy that Lord Kelvin did not know about. Kelvin had applied the perfectly good Law of Conservation of Energy without knowing all of the sources of energy. The main, long-lasting source of heat within the earth is radioactive decay, not shrinkage caused by gravitation. In the sun, it is nuclear fusion.

So when we speak of geothermal energy, volcanoes, hot springs, and the like, we are talking about nuclear energy. The mechanism involves radioactive decay, a process that is different from induced nuclear fission that occurs in our nuclear reactors, and fusion in the sun.

The earth has tremendous kinetic energy because of its high speed around the sun—30 kilometers per second (18 miles per second)—but there is no way to tap that energy, and if we could, it would change the orbit of the entire earth.

There is also a tremendous energy in the earth's magnetic field. We have no way to control it, but it is interesting to note that the magnetic field strength has been diminishing and the magnetic North Pole (as opposed to the geographic North Pole) has been wandering. Even now, scientists are keeping track of both the strength of the field and the direction. One wonders where the magnetic energy has gone, but the question is only academic. We have no way to extract any of that energy, and it is not entirely clear that we would want to do so if we could.

Generations have been taught that our coal, oil, and natural gas came from decaying plants and animals; indeed, the logo for Sinclair Oil remains the dinosaur. We know, for example, that "swamp gas," which is primarily methane, emerges from decay within the swamp.

It has been customary to call coal, oil, and natural gas *fossil fuels*, but with dubious justification. For example, it does not follow that the *only* source of methane is biological activity. Astronomers have long been able to show that methane is present in many bodies in the solar system. That methane cannot be explained by the concept of decaying trees and dinosaurs. Titan, a moon of Uranus, seems to have *oceans* of methane. There is considerable likelihood that the earth has been blessed with these fuels as well.

How we can and do utilize terrestrial energy

The simplest geothermal energy to use is the high-temperature energy found in places around the earth. In some cases, it is as simple as digging a well, blowing cold air down it and letting warm air return though another pipe to heat a building. I talked to a teacher in a Kansas grade school that had been heated that way for about a century. Eventually, extracting all that heat cooled down that the site so that it was no longer usable.

Of course, some places are hotter than others. The hotter spots can be used in a steam cycle to run machinery, the most useful of which is an electrical generator to send the electricity to remote places. Places near active volcanoes with steady lava flow are particularly useful in that regard. The flowing lava at sites in Hawaii keeps them replenished with heat energy.

Another way to use geothermal energy is much more subtle. We will discuss details later, but for now please recognize that there are *heat pumps* that can be used to transfer heat from the not-so-hot ground to heat a house. They can also be used with air conditioning houses in summer, transferring heat into the ground.

Ocean tides are caused by gravitational interactions between the sun, the moon, and the earth. The tidal phenomenon is present out in the open ocean but is far too small to be measured except by orbiting satellites that have clocks accurate to seconds per century. But there are *tidal basins*— certain geological structures—where that minuscule tide becomes channeled in such a way that tides can be extremely high. Notably, the high tide flowing into the Bay of Fundy causes the water level to rise by 60 feet (20 meters).   That is high enough to provide serious amounts of hydropower, but there are numerous reasons that the region has not been tapped.

The English Channel is a tidal basin of no outstandingly impressive statistics, but it has some bays on its sides where tides are adequate to produce power. The Rance Estuary in France comes to mind. New Zealand has also been able to tap tidal energy to some extent.

We get 85 percent of our energy from coal, oil, and natural gas. We do not know whether those fuels are actually "fossil fuels" or not, nor do we know how much reserve there is. So far, exploration has been based upon the dinosaur-and-rotting-vegetation model for the source, and it has served us for over a century. What we do know is that the earth has a large lode of combustible fuels. What we do not know is the extent. The quantity is clearly not infinite.

Aside from combustible fuels, there is one energy source that provides far more energy than all others in this class, and that is nuclear energy. There are 104 commercial nuclear reactors in the United States that provide about twenty percent of our electrical energy. Worldwide, there are over 400 reactors, not including the reactors that are used to propel a large number of our large Navy surface ships and submarines.

Properly used, the uranium lode of the earth could provide all of the energy used for all purposes for (very conservatively) a million years. This topic is discussed in Chapter 13.

The Sun

That bright shining globe in the sky sends us energy in many forms. Most prominent of all is the intense sunlight that lies in the visible region. Almost as prominent is infrared (IR) radiation that lies off the red end of the visible spectrum and ultraviolet (UV) radiation that lies off the violet end.

Not all of that radiation, either visible, IR or UV, reaches the surface of the earth. Much is reflected back into space by clouds. Much UV is absorbed by ozone—molecules containing three oxygen atoms, O_3—in the stratosphere.

Infrared radiation is absorbed by other molecules in the atmosphere, primarily water vapor, H_2O. Less important are the carbon dioxide molecule (CO_2) and methane (CH_4), the primary component of natural gas.

To some extent, the atmosphere also absorbs some visible radiation. Overall, the sunlight that reaches the earth's surface on a clear day at noon is only about 70 percent of the sunlight that reaches the outer envelope of the atmosphere.

There is an enormous magnetic field associated with the sun that extends well past Earth's orbit. That field has an effect on the climate, but cannot be tapped by any known means. The so-called "solar wind" affects the atmosphere and has been used to help propel spacecraft toward the outer reaches of the solar system; however, like many other forms of energy discussed in this chapter; it cannot be tapped.

How we can and do utilize the sun's energy

The "discovery of fire" was the invention of methods of setting fire to some form of *biomass*, defined for our purposes as being whatever results when something grows. (Sometimes, the term refers to the actual *quantity*, usually reckoned in tons or metric tons.) Dried leaves, twigs, and branches can be set alight. When man developed technology for cutting trees into firewood, this source of energy expanded dramatically.

In the late 1700s and early 1800s there was a thriving industry of killing right whales for their blubber for use in oil lamps. The ships at sea that heated the blubber to process to turn it into oil could be smelled for miles around. The population of right whales was severely diminished, and the species might well have been driven to extinction, but for the discovery of ways to extract a gas from coal to supply even more efficient lamps. The advent of petroleum assured that right whales would no longer be killed for their blubber.

Biomass is not limited to trees and whales, of course. We could grow grass, dry it in the sunlight, and used the dried grass for fuel. But we can also grow sugar cane, ferment the sugar into alcohol, and distill the liquid to remove the useful alcohol from the not-so-useful water. Some plants and algae also produce oils that can be used in lieu of diesel fuel.

Wind is caused by pressure differences, due ultimately to temperature differences caused by solar energy. When warm air meets cold air, the air moves. The first application of wind was to drive boats with sails a few thousand years ago. Later on, wind was used to drive rotating machines that were used for milling grain. They were called wind*mills*, though the term was later applied to machinery that pumped water out of the ground for farming purposes. Later yet, rotating wind-driven machinery was used for producing electricity. Generically, any such machinery is called a *wind turbine*. There are now enormous wind turbines capable of producing a few million watts of electricity.

Ocean waves, which are quite distinct from ocean tides, are produced by wind blowing over vast stretches of ocean. That there is a huge amount of energy in ocean waves has caught the attention of many an entrepreneur.

Hydropower is possible because solar energy has evaporated water. Some of that evaporated water obligingly falls on land at high elevation and forms into steams running down valleys. We can build dams to trap that water and use gravity to turn turbines.

Early water wheels were used for milling grain and running automatic looms for making fabric. Now the most common usage is to produce electricity.

It is easy to forget that the *source* of the energy driving our water machinery is the sun. Were it not for sunlight causing evaporation, that water would not be in the air and would not exist anywhere except the oceans.

Sunlight can be used directly for various purposes. We can build solar collectors that can be used for heating our homes and water. We can build devices called *photovoltaic* (PV) collectors that convert sunlight directly to electricity.

We can also build mirror systems that concentrate sunlight to provide high temperatures for running steam engines for producing electricity. There are large fields of such collectors in the Mojave Desert.

An important distinction can be made between two classes of solar energy. In one broad class, Mother Nature collects some solar energy. We can harvest what Mother Nature collects. Wind, waves, biomass, and hydro are examples.

On the other hand, Mother Nature does not manufacture PV cells, glass windows, or other such gadgets for us to collect solar energy directly, so we must make them ourselves. We can generate electricity with PV cells only where we put them, and we have to make them before we can put them anywhere.

Summary

We have classified energy sources into two broad categories and several subcategories. First, we have some energy simply because the earth is here with some lode of stored energy and second, we have energy that comes to us from space, primarily the sun. Of the solar energy sources, the two immediate subcategories are energy that Mother Nature collects and energy that we can collect only by building and installing devices that intercept sunlight.

Chapter 8   Hydropower Is Solar Power

Sunlight evaporates water. Clouds form. Precipitation falls. Water runs downhill. Hydropower plants use the weight of water behind dams to turn turbines to generate electricity. Hydropower, therefore, is solar power. It is efficient—over 85% for large power plants—and is as renewable as the rains. It's just the ticket for environmentalists.

Or so you'd think. During the Clinton Administration, EPA Head Carol M. Browner removed hydropower from the list of renewable energy sources. It may be renewable, and it may be solar, but hydropower is no longer politically correct. Hydropower—at least from dams large enough to produce a respectable amount of power—is no longer considered "Green." In this case, the untoward environmental effects of solar energy are explicitly noted. We shall encounter many paradoxical cases where the renewable energy turns out to have bad environmental consequences.

Figure 11 is a sketch showing the water flow in a typical hydropower plant. Water flows through the turbine, which rotates the shaft of the generator, producing electricity.

The amount of power available depends upon the volume flow rate of the water (cubic meters per second in SI Units). It also depends upon the elevation of the water surface in the reservoir—variously called the *hydraulic elevation*, the *head*, and the *pressure head*—above the river below the dam.

Hydropower plants can be turned on in a relative hurry, as there is no waiting time to heat up the system. They are therefore the preferred source of electricity for peak power, for example, during the hot afternoon while air conditioners are working very hard.

In July, 2001, the mayor of Seattle, Washington, was upset that President Bush was not willing to sign the Kyoto accords (that the Senate had already rejected 95:0 during the Clinton administration). The mayor declared that the city would begin immediately to reduce its CO_2 emissions. "We have plenty of hydropower," he said. (Grand Coulee's operators, whose electricity the good mayor is co-opting, must be wondering "Who's this *we*?")

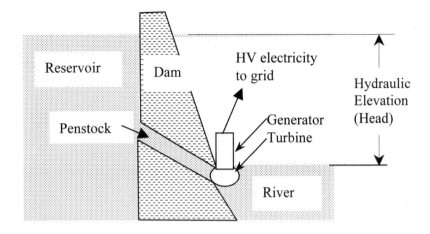

Figure 11: Generation of hydropower.

Pressure due to the water behind the dam forces water through the turbine, causing it to rotate, in turn rotating the generator. The amount of power produced depends upon the volume flow rate through the turbine and the elevation of the reservoir above the river below the dam.

Grand Coulee already produces all of the energy it can, and all that energy offsets the consumption of fuel somewhere. However, there is no *spare* energy to offset the consumption of *more* fuel, thereby to *reduce* CO_2 emissions in Seattle or elsewhere, even if the good mayor lays claim to the emission-free electricity.

Hydroelectric power plants produce high power for short times. While a hydro plant is producing power, the water level drops in the lake, because the flow rate through the turbines is usually greater than that of the streams that feed the lake. When the generator is turned off, the water level rises. Hydro plants are designed so that their year-round average power output is commensurate with the year-round water flow.

Large coal-powered and nuclear power plants typically produce 1000 MWe to 1200 MWe. The capacity of the very impressive Hoover Dam (*nee* Boulder Dam) on the Colorado River is 2079 MWe. (A picture of the somewhat smaller Glen Canyon Dam is shown in Fig. 12.) During 2000 (a typical year), Hoover produced 5.29 billion kWh, which means that its *average* output power was 604 MWe. Its *capacity factor* was 29.1%. That is, it produced 29.1% as much energy as a 2079 MWe power plant would produce if run at full power around the clock for a year.

The Hoover Dam collects the precipitation from a land area of 430,000 km², 60% larger than the land area of Colorado, storing it in Lake Mead. The total storage volume is 35 billion cubic meters. The *hydraulic elevation*—the height of the surface of the lake over the river below—is 175 m (576 feet).

Figure 12: The Glen Canyon Dam on the Colorado River.

The capacity is 1,296 MWe, and the average power output for a ten-year period is 570 MWe (capacity factor is 44%). Picture from http://www.nrel.gov/data/pix/searchpix.html, Larry Gordon, Bureau of Reclamation, photographer.

Hydropower in the US Energy Picture

It is interesting to look at the average power output per unit area, the so-called *energy intensity*. That is, Hoover Dam produces an average of 604 megawatts, but the water comes from 430,000 square kilometers. How much is that, expressed in watts per square meter of land collection area?

An incredibly small 0.0014 watts per square meter. Of course, getting hydropower from the runoff and using the land for other purposes are not necessarily mutually exclusive.

The Hoover Dam's collection area includes the arid Southwest. For the US as a whole, the capacity of all existing hydropower plants combined is 97,500 MWe, and their average electrical power production is 37,500 MWe. The average power intensity—37,500 MWe divided by 7.68 trillion square meters of US land area—is 0.0049 W/m^2, nearly three times that for Hoover Dam.

The energy intensities (either the 0.0014 W/m^2 or 0.0049 W/m^2) of the previous paragraphs should not be misinterpreted. The figures refer to the approximate amount of power that can be obtained from a huge tract of land that drains into a reservoir for a hydropower station. They specifically do not refer to the amount of land that is occupied by the reservoirs themselves.

As well, one can consider the actual land area flooded by the water behind the dam. For example Lake Powell, behind the Glen Canyon Dam, has 1,960 miles (3200 km) of shoreline, and covers 266 square miles (681 square kilometers or 681 million square meters.) The dam produced an average power of about 366 MW in 2004[15], so we may express the production as about 0.54 watts of average power for every square meter of lake surface.

The Bureau of Reclamation oversees the operation of 58 hydropower dams in the West, of which Grand Coulee is the largest. Its capacity[16] is about 6,500 MWe, and its average net generation is about 2,000 MWe, with an average capacity factor of a little over 30%. Its capacity factor in 2002 was 38%.

It is worth repeating that the low capacity factors for hydropower do not imply that these power plants are undependable. They are designed to produce lots of power for several hours per day when needed, but not continuously. The maximum power available—the capacity—is determined by the generators, but the year-round average power is determined by the annual rainfall.

The first large hydropower plant to be built was Niagara, which produced power first in 1882. It is obvious that engineers would first harness power from sites that offered a great deal of potential, as indeed they have. It becomes less and less cost-effective to build smaller and

---

[15] http://www.riversimulator.org/Resources/USBR/Hydropower.pdf
[16] http://www.commerce.wa.gov/_CTED/documents/ID_2015_Publications.pdf

smaller dams. I regard it as highly unlikely that the electrical output of hydro in the US could ever triple the current output.

Example: A Local Non-Solution

The annual rainfall in Connecticut, a state of about 13,000 km^2 (5000 mi^2) is about 1.1 meters (44 inches). Imagine collecting *all* of that water behind a dam of about 60-meter (200-foot) height. Doing so would inundate well over half the state, but we're just doing a calculation here, not planning to drown the Governor. (It would take years, of course, to fill the lake from rainfall, but we'll ignore that little problem.) How much around-the-clock power could we get?

About 225 MWe. Unfortunately, the state uses about 3,500 MWe around the clock. In other words, flooding over half the state with a dam holding water to 60-meter (200-foot) elevation would produce only about 6.5 percent of the state's electricity.

Worldwide Hydropower

Most of the world lags behind the US in energy production. All of our large hydropower sites are already in use, but elsewhere, there is power to be exploited. The Three Gorges project[17] will be the world's largest hydropower station when it is completed in 2009.

The Yangtze River is 5989 km long; only the Nile and the Amazon are longer. In terms of water flow, it ranks only behind the Amazon and the Congo.

The Three Gorges Dam will have twenty-six 700-MWe turbines for a total power output of 18,200 MWe, which is bigger by half than the world's present leader, Itaipu Dam on the Brazil-Paraguay border. The dam will stretch about two kilometers and be 175 meters high. The lake will be 600 km in length and will flood 28,000 hectares (280 square km, about 100 square miles). By comparison, the Glen Canyon Dam floods approximately the same area but its electrical capacity is only 1,300 MWe.

In addition, the dam will serve to control floods (two floods in 1931 and 1935, combined, killed nearly 300,000).

Whether dams do more harm than good may be endlessly debated, but this matter is certain: the existence of "clean" energy from hydroelectric dams is not necessarily of benefit to the environment. In other words, there are environmental complaints to be brought against solar energy.

---

[17] http://www.insidechina.com/special/damkey.php3

Utilities would gladly use more hydropower, *if* somebody could find a few more waterfalls. Hydropower is actually limited worldwide. I cite the Ehrlichs, who continue to tell us that solar energy is inadequate to supply our energy.

> "First, if all practical sites were utilized, hydropower would only generate 1 to 1.5 TW_e…"
>
> Paul & Anne Ehrlich (1991)

For comparison, we note that the US uses 3.3 TW_t of power (all types, not just electrical), and the world uses (2007) 15.8 TW_t, far more than the 1.5 TW_e that the Ehrlichs say that we can get worldwide from hydropower. In plain English, hydropower could not run the world, even if *all* practical sites were utilized.

Exercising Your Quads

Never having come to grips with the international system of units, the US government keeps track of energy production and consumption in quadrillion-BTU, known as *quads*. (One quad = 1.055 exajoules = 1.055 EJ.) Doing this disguises an interesting habit that most people might find amusing.

In 2008, says Table 1.2 "Energy Production by Source, 1949–2008," in the *EIA Annual Energy Review 2008*, the US produced 2.452 quads of energy from conventional hydropower. That's on page 7.

In the same book on page 230, "Electricity Net Generation: Total (All Sectors) 1949–2008," we find that hydro generated 248.1 billion kWh.

Let's look at the numbers. From the conversion factor above, 2.452 quads is equal to 2.587 EJ. Using one kWh = 3.6 million joules, we find that 248.1 billion kWh = 0.893 EJ. Careful study will reveal that 2.587 is not equal to 0.893. See table below.

There is nothing amiss with the conversion factors. The 248.1 billion kWh is accurate. The 2.452 quads is a fictitious, but useful, number to represent an as-if situation.

If the same 248.1 billion kWh of electrical energy had been produced by conventional (coal, oil, natural gas, nuclear, wood-fired) power plants, it would have required 2.587 EJ of heat, not the 0.893 EJ. The reason is that when fuels are consumed to produce electricity, there is invariably a heat engine involved, the purpose of which is to convert heat to work. The efficiency of doing so can never be 100% (see "Heat Engines" in Appendix B). For the entire US, the average efficiency of providing electricity to the grid by burning of fuels at power plants is 34%. Therefore, when the EIA discusses hydropower, they use one figure for energy *produced* (248.1 billion kWh = 0.893 EJ in 2008) and another (2.452 quads = 2.8587 EJ)—three times as large—for energy "*consumed*."

AER 2008		Conversion factor	SI unit
Table 1.2	2.452 quads "consumed"	$\times$ 1.055 EJ/quad	2.587 EJ
p. 230	248.1 billion kWh "produced" (actual energy generated)	$\times$ 3.6 $\times$ 10^6 J/kWh	0.893 EJ
2.587 EJ is the heat that would be required in average US power plants to produce 0.893 EJ.			

There is nothing wrong with this custom, so long as everybody knows what the EIA folks are doing and why. However, one has to read *The Annual Energy Review* very thoroughly to find out what they are doing. Moreover, the use of two different units, quads and billion kWh, for what is inherently one thing—energy—obfuscates the issue.

Who's Opposed to Hydropower?

It is axiomatic that people's lives are affected by hydropower, if only by mosquitoes, when hundreds of square miles are submerged by rising water behind dams. People who are personally affected naturally oppose such projects.

It is also true that other people benefit from having a dam on a river. Among them are people whose lands are otherwise regularly flooded in spring rains, people who enjoy water sports, and people who use the electricity from the dam.

Eventually—in a time span that may be decades or millennia—a dam silts up. That is, the reservoir behind the dam becomes loaded with silt instead of water. The silt has no effect on the elevation head (Fig. 11), but does limit the volume of water that may be stored. So long as the reservoir can hold enough water to produce peak-capacity power when needed, there is no problem. Eventual silting has sometimes been used by environmentalists[18] as an argument against building a hydropower plant—most notably the Aswan Dam in Egypt. The fact that silting can *in*

---

[18] http://cornerhouse.icaap.org/briefings/8.html

principle become a problem *eventually* is a poor argument. One needs to know, dam-by-dam, how much of a problem silting will be by when. The Mantilija Dam near Ventura, California, was evidently built in 1948 as a flood-control dam over the objections of the Army Corps of Engineers, partly on the grounds that it would soon silt up; it now has 6 billion cubic yards of sediment stored behind it. The dam is now being dismantled.

> "'The Matilija Dam,' Babbitt said then, 'is symbolic not only because it could become the largest dam to be taken down anywhere in the world, but also because it is a prime example of dams that are environmentally harmful as well as useless.'"
>
> Texas A&M University[19]

Suffice it to say that dams are routinely opposed on environmental grounds, either because they "destroy" the landscape, block fish migration routes, or block the normal paths of land animals.

> "In 1976 Leiderman ran for Congress from Missouri…primarily against the Meremec Dam project…"
>
> Berman & O'Connor (1996)

The energy source is renewable, yet it has run into opposition from environmentalists.

---

[19] http://twri.tamu.edu/watertalk/archive/2000-Dec/Dec-28.3.html

Chapter 9   Wind Power Is Solar Power

Heat from the sun is the source of energy for the winds, but it is not high temperature *per se* that drives the wind. For example, the Great Red Spot on Jupiter—a place not exactly well known for tropical vacations—is a cyclonic storm that has persisted for hundreds of years. Rather, it is temperature *gradients* that are responsible for moving the air.

In recent years, wind power has become a national fad, complete with a barrage of headlines, full-length newspaper articles, and editorials waxing eloquent about wind-generated electricity. The flyers that come with our utility bills have been encouraging us to pay extra for energy from the Clean Green Machine.

Wind Power Is Ancient. Wind-Generated Electricity is New

A picture on a piece of pottery dating from about BC 4000 shows Egyptian boats with square sails. By AD 640, wind turbines were at work in Persia grinding grain, and wind-driven gristmills have been used in Normandy since about 1180. Dutch wind turbines, used for pumping water out to the ocean, are a national symbol. Multi-bladed wind turbines have long been used on American farms for drawing water from wells. Great improvements in wind turbines followed the improvements in propeller design in World War-II. Some six thousand years after the first recorded use of wind power, we have taken the step of attaching a generator to the wind turbine to produce electricity.

Electricity is the most useful power we have, and it has been obvious for a century that wind turbines could somehow be fitted with electrical generators. The engineering problems were difficult. Most generators were designed to rotate fast, typically 3600 RPM, but such high rotation rates could only be accomplished with small-diameter wind turbines that would not be capable of producing much power.

The problem of producing electricity from the slow rotation of huge wind turbines has been addressed in two ways. Some machines have transmissions to cause rapid rotation of their generators from slow turbine rotation. Others now use modified permanent-magnet generators that rotate at the slow rate of the turbine. (Permanent magnets that can withstand the vibrations and temperature variations of an outdoor wind turbine are a comparatively recent invention.)

In the United States in 2008, wind generated 52 billion kWh of electrical energy, about 1.3 percent of the 4110.3 billion kWh generated in the country. Obviously, there has to be a reason *or reasons* that we don't get more power from the wind. Let us look at the underlying physics.

How Wind Turbines Work

If we are to extract energy from the wind, then the wind must have energy to begin with. That energy is *kinetic energy*, the energy the wind has because the air is moving. We can extract no more energy from the wind than the wind has.

When we extract energy from the wind, we reduce the speed of the air. However, we cannot *stop* the wind entirely—extracting all of its energy—because doing so would block incoming wind from reaching our wind turbine.

Wind Turbines, Old and New

Picture a sailing ship in a stiff wind, and you can just see the sails billowed out and you can almost feel the great force exerted on the sail by the wind. It is easy to picture why early wind turbines were built with huge canvas sails. Unfortunately, what works for sailing ships is not necessarily the best scheme for wind turbines.

High efficiency for wind turbines involves relatively thin blades that bear no resemblance to ships' sails. Modern wind turbines with two or three blades rotate more rapidly than multi-bladed farm wind turbines. Here, we are talking about angular speed, the number of rotations per minute.

Typically, the tips of the blades move about five or six times as fast as the wind. In moderate wind, they move about the speed of a car on the highway. You might even wonder how they could possibly get much energy out of the wind, because there is so little surface area for the wind to hit. Perhaps surprisingly, they are much more efficient than the old sail-type wind turbines and the multi-bladed wind turbines seen on farms.

A Wind Turbine's Job Is to Stop the Air

Figure 13 is a very crude drawing of a wind turbine seen from the side, with wind blowing from left to right. If the job is to extract the kinetic energy of the wind, then the wind must be stopped! However, if we do stop the wind, then (by definition) the air in the vicinity of the wind turbine stops completely. Therefore, the main idea behind wind turbines is that they extract *some* of the energy in the wind, slowing down the air in the process.

A little thought will reveal a small problem: how can you move high-speed air into the wind turbine when the "used-up" air leaves slowly? The answer to this dilemma is that the air leaving the wind turbine spreads out, somewhat as shown in Figure 13. The amount of air leaving the wind turbine at low velocity must equal the amount of air arriving at the wind turbine at high velocity; therefore, it spreads out into a wider area. If a metric ton (1000 kg) of air comes to the wind turbine in one second, then a metric ton must leave the wind turbine in one second.

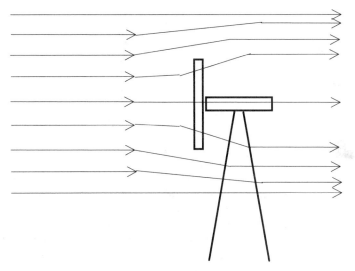

Figure 13: The wind pattern for a wind turbine.

Because the air must leave with some velocity (hence some energy), only *some* of the kinetic energy is taken by the wind turbine. It turns out that only 16/27 (about 59%)[20] of the energy carried by the wind *could* be extracted by a *perfect* wind turbine; the very best real wind turbines peak out at about 50% efficiency, and only under ideal conditions.

How can skinny un-sail-like blades accomplish this task? Simply by moving fast. ("Skinny" is a relative term. The width of the blades at the end is equal to the height of a man.) At a given moment, the blade is somewhere blocking the air, and slowing down the air in a column behind the blade. But the blade is moving, and is soon blocking air elsewhere, extracting the energy from a new column of air. During the time the blade is not blocking the air in a given column, the air speed begins to increase again. However, before the wind speed has picked up significantly, the rapidly moving blade is there to take its energy again.

---

[20] See, for example, E. Wendell Hewson, "Electrical Energy from the Wind, pp. 6-142 – 6-174, in *Energy Technology Handbook,* Douglas M. Considine, P.E., Editor, (McGraw-Hill, 1977). The limiting efficiency is called the *Betz Limit.*

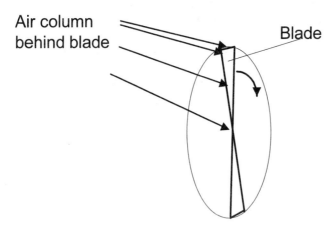

Figure 14: A thin blade blocks a column of air.

By this reasoning, the faster the wind turbine turns, the more efficient the wind turbine will be. However, as the wind turbine turns faster, the very blades that are extracting energy from the wind act like a fan to propel the wind, giving energy back to it. Therefore, the fan shouldn't turn *too* fast. That is, there is some ideal rotation rate for the wind turbine for any given wind speed. For multi-bladed wind turbines, the ideal rotation rate is low, and the efficiency is also very low.

Propeller Size and Wind speed

An excellent wind turbine might have nearly 50% efficiency. That is, it can convert 50% of the kinetic energy of the air that passes through it into mechanical energy. (Engineers refer to the figure as the *power coefficient*.) But how much kinetic energy can there be when the density of air is so low, about 1.27 kg per cubic meter, about one seven-hundredth the density of water? Obviously, it is necessary to intercept a lot of wind.

The interested reader may wish to consult the Wind Power section in Appendix B to see how wind turbine power is figured out. For a wind turbine whose diameter is D, the power output is P_{out} when the wind speed is v, and the efficiency is η. The equation is

$$P_{out} = 0.5\eta D^2 v^3 \qquad \text{Eq. 1}$$

For an excellent wind turbine (usually of two blades) the efficiency is almost 50%; most large three-bladed wind turbines have a overall maximum efficiency (wind-to-electricity) of about 40%. Two-bladed wind turbines can in principle have higher efficiency than three-bladed ones.

However, almost all industrial wind turbines are three-bladed, because they have better dynamic stability.[21]

Figure 15 shows plots of wind turbine power versus wind speed for a 75-meter diameter turbine, as represented by Eq. 1. Three efficiencies are shown, 59% (the Betz limit, which is the maximum theoretical power), 50%, and 40% (which pretty accurately represents the GE 1.5-MW units). There is also a curve for the same turbine fitted with a 2-MW generator.

Notice several features. Up to the speed at which maximum power is reached, the power is proportional to the cube of wind speed. Real wind turbines actually produce no power at very low speeds, say below about 4 m/s. At such low speeds, it makes very little difference whether it produces power or not. Figure 15 shows a rather abrupt change from the curve to the flat portions of the power curves, but in reality the transition is made more smoothly.

Through the flat region, from 12 or 13 m/s to 25 m/s, the output power is held constant at the maximum rating of the attached generator. The method for doing so is to "trim" the blades (rotate them on their axes) so as to make them less efficient. For example, at just under 25 m/s, the power output of the real generators would be about 17 MW if the blades were adjusted for maximum efficiency.

What would be the effect of using a 2-MW$_e$ generator instead of a 1.5-MW generator? When the wind speed is up, there would be more power available, as shown in Fig. 15. However the wind does not reach that speed very often. The price to pay for having the larger generator is (A) having to lift the larger generator up to the nacelle; (B) having to build a stronger support structure; (C) having to pay more for the generator and the support structure; (D) having to install and pay for heavier wires; and (E) having a lower capacity factor. This last disadvantage comes from the fact that the larger generator does not increase the average power very much over the course of a year. Compared with the nameplate power ratings of 1.5 and 2 MW gives a higher capacitor factor for the smaller generator.

Actual power curves for industrial wind turbines of various sizes are available from sales brochures at the websites of General Electric (www.gewind.com) and Vestas (www.vestas.com). Each and every one shows a minimum ("cut-in") speed where the turbine begins to produce power, a v^3 region up to the point where full power is achieved, and constant power to 25 m/s. (They do not show the curve dropping to zero in high winds, but the data are in tables.)

---

[21] The moments of inertia about any two axes in the plane of the blades are equal.

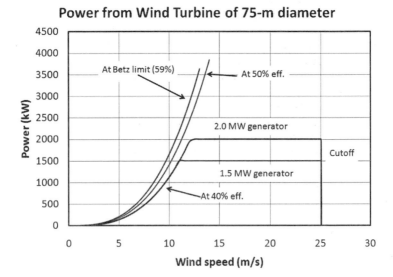

Figure 15: Wind power versus wind speed for a hypothetical 75-m diameter wind turbine.

The upper curve represents the power that could be obtained by a wind turbine operating at the maximum possible efficiency, 59% (the Betz limit), at all wind speeds. The second curve represents a more realistic (but still high) 50% efficiency. The third curve shows the power output for a realistic wind turbine fitted with a 2MW$_e$ generator. The bottom curve shows the power output if the turbine has a 15-MW$_e$ generator.

Nameplate Power and Capacity Factor

Capacity factor is a matter or engineering design. Imagine putting a 1-MW generator on a turbine the size of a pinwheel. The average power will be zero, and so will be the capacity factor. Now imagine putting a 5-watt generator (like the one on a little hand-crank flashlight) on a turbine of 75-meter diameter. It should almost always possible to generate 5 watts, so the capacity factor would be nearly 100%. So it is simply a matter of scaling the size of the generator to the size of the turbine.

Depending upon where we put our hypothetical 75-m diameter wind turbine, the annual output might be, say, 5 million kWh with the 2-MW$_e$ generator attached, but might be 4.5 million kWh with the 15-MW$_e$ generator. That is, the smaller generator gives somewhat less energy over the course of a year, but the power output can be held constant over a slightly wider range of wind speed. "Wind-site Predictions" on page 202 in

Appendix B gives a more thorough description of the relationship between wind speed, turbine size, generator capacity, and capacity factor. In the heady days of California's wind farms, the emphasis was on high nameplate power. ("High" meant perhaps 200 kW at the time.) In those days, they routinely put large generators on small turbines and wound up with capacity factors of about 20%. Nowadays, with the same turbines, they would use the 100-kW generator instead of the 200-kW to obtain a higher capacity factor and more steady power, at the expense of some annual energy.

It is interesting to compare the capacity factors of wind turbines with those of nuclear power plants. Figure 16 shows three-year capacity factors from *Nuclear News*[22] for all of the 104 nuclear power generators in the US along with a horizontal line representing a 35% capacity factor for wind turbines. Forty-seven of the nukes have capacity factors greater than 90%. With only two exceptions, all nuclear power plants have more than double the 35%-capacity factors of *new, up-to-date* wind farms with the fanciest wind turbines. The only two exceptions are Davis-Besse, which was out of commission for two years while the reactor head was replaced, and Browns-Ferry-1, which is undergoing a complete rebuilding.

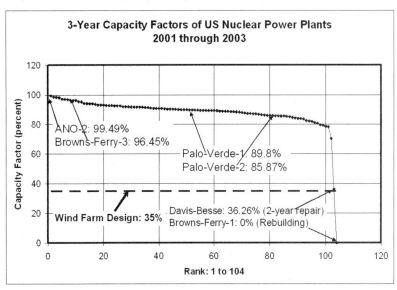

Figure 16: Three-year capacity factors of US nuclear power plants for the years 2001 through 2003.

---

[22] E. Michael Blake, "U.S. capacity factors: Still on the rise," *Nuclear News* pp. 25-29, (May 2004).

Case Study 1: Lake Benton I, Minnesota

Lake Benton Power Partners, LLC, operates a wind farm at Lake Benton, Minnesota, consisting of one hundred forty-three 750-kW$_e$ (nameplate) Enron wind turbines for a capacity of 107 MWe. The annual generation is 327,000 megawatt-hours. This corresponds to a capacity factor of 34.9%. (Enron is out of business.)

The Enron wind turbines have a radius of 23 meters. According to Eq. 1, they should produce 750 kW$_e$ at a wind speed of 11.2 meters/second, which is about 25 miles per hour. The wind turbines are designed to withstand ferocious winds of 59.5 meters per second, equivalent to 133 miles per hour. However, the machines shut down when the wind speed reaches about 25 m/s. A hypothetical wind turbine of 23-meter radius operating at 50% efficiency could produce 8300 kW$_e$, well in excess of 750 kW$_e$. However, it would be subject to extreme forces. The wind turbines are designed to produce the 750 kW$_e$ at all speeds between 11.2 m/s and 25 m/s. At the higher wind speeds, the pitch of the blades is adjusted to reduce the efficiency of the turbine, so as not to exceed the nameplate power of the generator. By 25 m/s, the efficiency is down to about 4.5%. Little is lost, however, as the wind speed is rarely that high.

We will look at nine other case studies later on.

Caveat Emptor: Availability Factor

The term *availability* takes on a different meaning for wind power than it does for other sources of power. For most power sources the *availability factor* represents the fraction of time that the power is available when you need it.

For example, suppose that a hydropower station is ready at all times to produce power when it is needed. Then its *availability factor* would be 100%. As we saw in Chapter 8, the average load factor of hydropower stations in the US is 29.1%, but that factor comes entirely from patterns of usage. (They are designed to produce lots of power for short times.)

For another example, in a nuclear power plant, the plant is running at full power all of the time that it runs at all, typically 90% of the time. In that case, the availability factor and the capacity factor are the same, both 90%. (Recently, the three-year capacity factors for the 104 US nuclear power plants in operation is 90%.)

Power stations used at times of peak load only may operate, say, 20% of the hours during the year, but could possibly be ready at all times to turn on immediately. For a station like this one, the load factor would be 20%, but the availability factor would be 100%. The power is there when you need it.

For wind farms, the term *availability factor* means the fraction of time the machine is ready to run *if the wind blows*. Wind turbines, by this definition, usually have high availability factors. As an extreme example, a mechanically and electrically perfect wind turbine sitting in an always-windless location would have an availability factor of 100% even though it never produces any electricity at all. If *availability* were defined in the same way for wind turbines as for other power stations, the figure would usually equal the capacity factor.

Constraints

In short, the wind turbine can extract *some* of the energy from the air that intercepts the wind turbine's blades. The obvious facts are:
- the larger the wind turbine, the more power it can generate;
- the faster the wind, the more power is available;
- that wind turbines can't be placed one behind the other;
- that the side-to-side spacing of wind turbines should accommodate the spread-out of air behind the wind turbines;
- that the wind turbines should be high off the ground;
- and that wind turbines must accommodate to varying wind speed.

Just as true are the not-so-obvious facts:
- there is always some wind speed above which the wind turbine must be stopped, lest it fly apart;
- that the power output of our hypothetical wind turbine is highly variable with wind speed;
- that the most efficient wind turbines have the fewest blades; however, three-bladed ones are more stable dynamically than 2-bladed ones.
- that very large wind turbines introduce annoying ground vibrations,
- and that the power output from the huge wind farms in California is a tiny fraction of California's needs.

Placement of the wind turbine

Proud citizens often like to point to a large wind turbine up on a hill and tell their visitors that the city gets a lot of their power from that lovely apparatus. Others may object that the machine is ugly. We do not intend to concern ourselves with aesthetics: if the wind turbine produces necessary power, then beauty is a secondary consideration. Do we complain about the looks of the cows that give us milk?

Far more important is the amount of wind at the site. In very approximate terms, if one site has average winds of 5 meters per second and another has average winds of 8 meters per second, the latter site will produce 4 times as much electrical power.[23] Lest there be any doubt about this matter, a research wind turbine at the University of Massachusetts was recently moved from a convenient hill near the campus to a higher hill some twenty miles away for precisely that reason.

Wind sites are classified according to the mean annual power density of the winds. "Areas designated 'good' are roughly equivalent to an estimated mean annual power, at 10 meter height, of 200 to 300 Watts per square meter (W/m^2), and 'excellent' if more than 300 W/m^2," according to a California Energy Commission report.[24] However, the average power that might be produced there would depend upon the design of the wind turbines, as we saw in Fig. 15 and associated discussion.

Arrangement for Wind Farms

It is important to understand that wind power-density figures for wind sites do not refer to land area, but instead to the cross-sectional area intercepted by the spinning wind turbine's blades. Wind turbines cannot be lined up one directly behind the other because the slow air emerging from one wind turbine is of no use to the one behind. Moreover, the turbulence of a wind turbine can destroy the one behind. Good engineering practice requires that rows of wind turbines be about ten diameters apart. That is, if each wind turbine has a 20-meter diameter, for example, the rows of wind turbines have to be about 200 meters apart.

Moreover, wind turbines cannot be lined up tip-to-tip, both for reasons of wind-slowing (See Fig. 13) and turbulence. Here, engineering practice is determined by the wind direction. If there is a prevailing wind direction, then the wind turbines can be placed about three diameters apart, 60 meters for our wind turbine of 20-meter diameter, in a direction perpendicular to the prevailing wind direction. That is, our wind turbine would sit in the middle of an area whose size is 200 meters by 60 meters, or 12,000 square meters.

What happens if we use larger wind turbines, say, 40 meters in diameter instead of 20 meters? According to the wind turbine formula (Eq. 1) we would get four times as much power at any given wind speed. But the distance between rows of wind turbines would have to be 400 meters instead of 200, and the tip-to-tip distance would have to be 120 meters. That is, the 40-m diameter wind turbine would sit in the middle of an area of 400 meters by 120 meters, or 48,000 square meters. These larger wind turbines have four times the power of the smaller ones, but the

---

[23] See Appendix B, "Wind-site Predictions"

[24] A. Miller and R. Simon, *Wind Power Potential in California,* San Jose State University, prepared for the California Energy Commission, May 1978.

required land area is also four times as big. The result is that wind turbines can get just so much power out of a given land area.

The arithmetic is not hard to work out. If the average power density in the wind is 300 watts per square meter facing the wind, one may expect to extract about 4 watts per square meter of land area. That is, for a site with wind turbines lined up in rows that are perpendicular to the prevailing winds, you may simply divide the average power density of the winds by 75 to get the average power per unit land area.

The arrangement of wind turbines is not the same when there is no prevailing wind direction. If the winds might come from the south one day and from the east the next, then the wind turbines that were beside on another on one day have become ahead and behind on the next. For this case, the wind turbines have to be ten diameters apart in all directions.

For our example of 20-meter diameter wind turbines, the wind turbines should be 200 meters apart in both directions. For this case, 300 watts per square meter facing the wind results in about 1.2 watts per square meter of land area. The rule of thumb we have developed is to take the average wind power density and divide by 250 to get the power per unit land area.

The Environmental Protection Agency[25] is in agreement with these figures. It says:

> "Contemporary wind projects are typically rated at 25 to 100 MW[e]. A 25 MW[e] project might have 60 to 70 turbines covering 1500 acres. [This amounts to 16,700 watts per acre, or 4.1 W/m^2, and refers to capacity, not average output.]. Turbines, while reminiscent of aircraft propellers, are specifically designed for electrical generation. The blade and generator housing, or nacelle, pivots to face directly into the wind. Each turbine is rated at about 300 to 500 kW[e] of *capacity*. [60 × 400 kW[e] (capacity) = 24 MW[e] (capacity)] Turbines are usually arranged in rows oriented at right angles to the direction of the prevailing winds and spaced at two to five rotor diameters from each other. Rows of turbines are usually located with roughly 10 rotor diameters between them." Wind projects typically produce power about 95 percent of the time at an average output of 28 - 35 percent of rated capacity." [emphasis and brackets added]

At a 30% capacity factor, the EPA's estimate works out to 1.23 W/m^2 of land area.

The EPA comment above is somewhat old. There are now large wind turbines that are capable of a few megawatts. Typically, they have a hub

---

[25] http://www.epa.gov/globalwarming/publications/actions/state/wa/mitigatef.html

height of 50 to 100 meters and diameters of 50 to 80 meters. But the average power per unit of land area remains the same.

Case Study 2: Navitas/Minnesota

Navitas Energy, LLC, has received permission to erect eighty-seven 1.5-MWe wind turbines, for a total nameplate power of 130.5 MWe on a parcel of land consisting of 10,000 acres in Murray and Pipestone Counties, Minnesota. This translates to a peak power density of 3.22 watts per square meter of land area. With a capacity factor of 35%, this would amount to an average of 1.13 watts per square meter of land area.

Case Study 3: Chanarambie/Minnesota

Chanarambie Power Partners, LLC, has received permission to erect sixty-one 1.5-MWe wind turbines, for a total nameplate power of 91.5 MWe on a parcel of land consisting of 6,500 acres in Murray Counties, Minnesota. This translates to a peak power density of 3.48 watts per square meter of land area. With a capacity factor of 35%, this would amount to an average of 1.22 watts per square meter of land area.

Case Study 4: Big Spring, Texas

Big Spring, Texas, is home to a wind farm of 42 Vestas V47 wind turbines rated at 660 kW$_e$, and four Vestas V66 wind turbines rated at 1.65 MW$_e$. They are spread out in three groups on 23 square km (9 square miles) of land on a mesa. The nameplate energy intensity is therefore about 1.5 W/m^2. The capacity factor for the installation is 34%, so the average power production amounts to 0.51 W/m^2. Lightning is responsible for 4% of the downtime. Hail damage can be reduced by stopping the rotation during a hailstorm. The tips of the blades normally move at 70 m/s; adding that to the 55 m/s hail speed would increase the relative velocity of the hail to 125 m/s. Such high velocity hail would cause severe damage to the blades.

Case Study 5: Kotzebue, Alaska

Kotzebue, Alaska, is just north of the Arctic circle, and is accessible only by air and water. The town has 3000 residents.

A wind farm outside of town has ten Atlantic Orient Corporation 66-kW$_e$ turbines sitting on a 148-acre site. The nameplate energy intensity is therefore 1.1 W/m^2. In service, the site produced an average of 83.6 kW$_e$, equivalent to an average power density of 0.14 W/m^2. In this installation, the wind turbines are spread out rather widely. The capacity factor for the installation is 12.6%.

The weather in Kotzebue is very dry, and icing of the propellers has not been a problem.

Case Study 6: Green Mountain, Vermont

The Green Mountain wind project is small even by wind farm standards. Its capacity is 6.05 MWe, and it has a 24.6% capacity factor. In other words, its year-round average power is 1.5 MWe. As the eleven 550-kW$_e$ wind turbines are more or less single-file along a 1.2-km line on a mountain ridge, it makes little sense to speak of the land area. The *linear* power density is 5 kW$_e$/meter. That figure might be useful for other ridge applications.

Vermont presents special problems owing largely to weather. Over 25% of the downtime was due to lightning damage. In one case, it destroyed one blade of a wind turbine. In fact, there was lightning damage about three times per year. There are about 1700 unscheduled maintenance events per year. Bad weather in the winter delayed the repairs to two wind turbines by several months. Icing has a severe impact on performance, but only for short times.

Case Study 7: South Dakota

There is a plan to put a 3000-MWe (nameplate) wind farm in South Dakota on 350 square miles of land. The nameplate energy intensity is 3.3 W/m^2. If they are lucky enough to have a 35% capacity factor, they will produce electrical energy at the rate of 1.16 W/m^2.

Case Study 8: Lamar, Colorado

The Lamar wind farm in Southeastern Colorado has 108 1.5-MW wind turbines, standing 262 feet (80 meters) tall. According to *The Pueblo Chieftain*,[26] the turbines are spread out over 11,840 acres (4800 hectares). The *peak* power density will be 3.38 kW/m^2 (13,700 watts per acre); at 30% capacity factor, this would be 1.01 W/m^2 (4100 watts per acre). At 36% capacity factor (don't hold your breath), the wind farm would produce year-round average power of 1.2 W/m^2 (4900 watts per acre).

Case Study 9: Altamont Pass, California

Altamont Pass in Alameda and Contra Costa counties, California, has a variety of older (1983) and newer wind (1990) turbines with a capacity of 268.7 MW, located on about 100 square miles (256 square km). The annual production is estimated to be 392.2 million kWh.[27] These numbers amount

---

[26] Anthony Mestas, "Wind farm generating electricity near Lamar," *The Pueblo Chieftain* (January 9, 2004). The title is incorrect. The wind farm was still undergoing testing.

[27] "Summary of Visits to Wind Power Projects in Five States," Appendix IV, General Accounting Office (GAO-04-756 Renewable Energy), 2004.

to a production of 0.17 W/m^2 (700 average watts per acre), and an annual capacity factor of 16.6%.

Case Study 10: High Winds Energy Center, Solano County, CA

This Solano County site in California is still under construction.[27] In Phase I, 81 turbines will be installed; phase II will add 9 more, for a total installed capacity of 162 MW on 6,500 acres (2630 ha). The expected annual generation will be 480 million kWh. These numbers amount to an average production of 2.08 W/m^2 (8.4 kW/acre), and an expected annual capacity factor of 33.8%.

Scaling It Up

From the analysis and cases above, it is evident that wind farms can generate electrical power at the rate of about 1.2 W/m^2 for most good sites and up to about 4 W/m^2 in the rare sites where the wind always comes from one direction. (I have been unable to find any wind farms that approach this theoretical figure.)

Now, suppose the goal is to generate enough energy to average 1000 MWe around the clock, the power output of one typical traditional power plant.   At 1.2 W/m^2, the land-area requirement is about 833 square kilometers, or 300 square miles.

Let us put that land area into perspective. Imagine a 1.6-km (one-mile) wide swath of wind turbines extending from San Francisco to Los Angeles. That land area is what would be required to produce as much power around the clock as one large coal, natural gas, or nuclear power station that normally occupies about one square kilometer of land.

But the story does not end there, because California uses an average of 30.3 GW$_e$. To produce that much power would require 7,500 square kilometers (3000 square miles) of wind turbines in good-to-excellent sites with a prevailing wind direction or 25,000 square kilometers (10,000 square miles) of land area with strong winds but no prevailing direction. For comparison, that is twice the land area of Connecticut. If there were enough wind throughout the area, the 30.3 GW$_e$ could be generated with a 48-km (29-mile) swath of wind turbines between San Francisco and Los Angeles.

The scenario for getting an average of 30.3 MW$_e$ for California is quite unrealistic for other reasons. There would be times when every wind turbine produced full power, which is approximately three times the average power. In other words, they could produce an excess of 70 GWe; California couldn't use that power, nor could the power be shipped terribly far to, say, Chicago. The grid was not designed to carry the load, and isn't up to the task. Therefore, the output of the wind turbines would have to be cut back by 2/3. The overall capacity factor would suffer. Therein lies one reason that wind turbines can't provide a huge percentage of the average electrical power on the grid.

The experience of Denmark, which produces the most wind energy per capita, is illuminating. An uncritical look at the numbers shows that Denmark produces 19 percent of its electrical energy from wind. A more careful look shows that Denmark produces only about 9.7% of the electrical energy used in the country. This apparent contradiction needs to be considered carefully. Let us quote from *Wind Energy: The Case Of Denmark*[28],

> Over the last eight years West Denmark has exported (couldn't use), on average, 57% of the wind power it generated and East Denmark an average of 45%. The correlation between high wind output and net outflows makes the case that there is a large component of wind energy in the outflow indisputable.

The Danes are saying here that when wind power is high, they export power rather than use it. West Denmark and East Denmark are not interconnected. West Denmark connects to Southern Sweden, Southern Norway, and Germany. East Denmark connects to Southern Sweden, but considerably farther south than the West Denmark tie-in. But in all cases, the power fed in from Denmark is a small fraction of the power on the grid. Especially interesting is that Norwegian and Swedish hydropower are very helpful in stabilizing the grid.

Of course, Norway, Sweden, and Germany all have access to power that is relatively cheap, so they are not willing to pay a premium for Danish wind power. As a consequence, Danes citizens pay a high price for electricity exported at low cost.

Altamont Pass in California is one particularly good site for wind turbines, at least according to my experience there in July, 2001 when the wind was howling. Clearly, the wind power density there is much higher than it is over the billions of square meters (thousands of square miles) that would be required to produce a significant fraction of California's electricity.

---

[28] *Wind Energy: The Case Of Denmark*, Center for Politiske Studier, (September, 2009).

Figure 17: A few of the wind turbines at Altamont Pass in California.

It is true, of course, that wind turbines have a relatively small footprint. That is, although a 100-MWe (average power) wind farm might occupy 100 square kilometers, the windmill towers themselves cover only, say, 1 square kilometer. The land can be used for farming or ranching at the same time.

Nevertheless, the visual effect is stunning. Make no mistake about it, even a small wind farm is an impressive sight. Figure 17 shows a few of the hundreds of wind turbines at Altamont Pass, elevation 300 meters (1000 feet), east of Livermore, California. The site has no trees, and receives strong ocean breezes. It is apparent to the casual visitor that the machinery is huge and hazardous.

There are times when the wind is calm *everywhere*. At those times, all of the power would have to come from somewhere else. Engineers are fond of saying that wind turbines "provide energy but not power." It's jargon, to be sure, but they have a point. Wind turbines do most assuredly reduce the use of fuel; however, they do not allow a utility to get rid of so much as one power plant. The utilities must maintain full reserve to handle the situation when the wind does not blow. In other words, wind turbines do not add meaningful capacity to a system.

To put it fairly, but bluntly, wind power can never produce more than a small fraction of our electricity.

"But, like hydropower, wind power can make only a modest contribution to save us from the energy trap. If the windiest 3 percent of Earth's land area were covered with efficient wind turbines (a gigantic undertaking), only about 1 TW[e] of electricity might be generated..."

Paul & Anne Ehrlich (1991)

Small Units for Home and Farm

Wind turbines are probably the cheapest source of energy for most remote applications. The utility is perfectly happy to run power lines to a customer who will be using a megawatt of power, but it's awfully expensive to run power lines 50 kilometers to a farm or home that will use no more than a few kilowatts.

A home that gets its electricity from a wind turbine needs deep-discharge batteries to supply power when the wind isn't blowing, and a big-enough wind turbine to recharge the batteries and run the household when the winds are up. The installation is usually expensive, but nowhere near the cost of running long power lines from the utility. I know of one mountain household near Westcliffe, Colorado, that is not connected to the grid at all. The owners use a combination of wind and photovoltaics. They have lots of big batteries to store electrical energy. They also have to be prudent in their consumption of power. They are proud to be able to survive without the electricity from the grid, but would tie into the grid in a heartbeat if they had the opportunity.

Figure 18 shows the performance of a commercial 1-kW$_e$ wind turbine that uses a modified automotive alternator as its electrical generator. It produces about 1 kilowatt between wind speeds of 11 m/s and 20 m/s. Just like its larger cousins, this unit is designed to have relatively constant output at wind speeds above about 10 m/s. At the lower wind speeds, however, the efficiency is about half that of large commercial units.

A Few More Problems

The Wind Turbine Meets the Power Line

The wind rotates the turbine and the generator produces electricity. How is the turbine's electricity to be matched to that of the utility? Imagine that you have two wires, one in each hand. One wire has electricity provided by the utility and the other wire's electricity comes from a wind turbine (or, for that matter, from any other source). Your job is to connect the wires so that there is no spark.

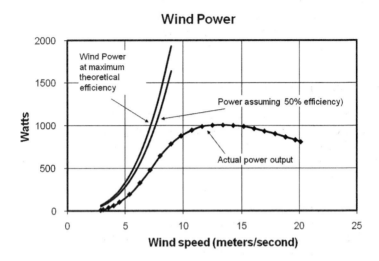

Figure 18: The performance of a commercial 1-kW$_e$ wind turbine.

If—at all times—the voltage on the wire in your left hand is identical to the voltage on the wire in your right hand, the wires may be connected together without any sparks. The voltage on a 115-VAC power line varies from +163 volts [29] to −163 volts in 1/120 second and back to + 163 volts during the next 1/120 second. (The AC voltage has the same heating power as 115 volts DC.)

The wind turbine's voltage, to be properly tied to the power line, should have exactly the same voltage, exactly the same frequency, and exactly the same timing in order to match the power line voltage. In the case of large turbines, the voltage to be matched is the high voltage of the transmission line, but the principles are the same—the output voltage of the generator must match the power-line voltage at all times.

Three techniques have been used to provide the match. In one, induction motors have been run as generators, with the AC power line providing a rotating magnetic field in the generator. The RPM is controlled by the pitch of the blades. In a related system, variable "slip" (see next

---

[29] A 115-VAC power line makes a light bulb burn just as brightly as a 115-volt battery does. Since the A.C. voltage varies from positive to negative and is low most of the time, it is clear that the voltage must exceed 115 volts considerably for some of the time. In fact, the voltage rises to $115\sqrt{2}$ = 163 volts, and goes negative by that amount as well.

paragraphs) also uses the AC power, but introduces variable slip to allow for variations in RPM. Finally, DC generators (often using permanent magnets) can generate DC, which can be converted electronically to AC to match the power line.

Pardon, your slip is showing.

In a typical induction motor such as the one in a washing machine, the line voltage causes a magnetic field to rotate at 3600 rotations per minute (60 cycles per second), but the rotor rotates at 3450 rotations per minute, being dragged along by the moving magnetic field. The difference, 150 revolutions per minute, is called the *slip RPM*, and the fraction (3600 – 3450)/3600 = 0.042, or 4.2%, is called the *slip*. A typical four-pole motor (Fig. 19) turns at 1725 RPM, but the field rotates at 1800 RPM, making the slip also 4.2%.

In an induction *generator*, somewhat the same principles apply, but the applied torque (from a steam generator, for example) causes the rotor to rotate *faster* that 3600 RPM. That is, the slip is present, but of opposite sign. The rotor is ahead, not behind.

In wind-driven induction systems, multi-pole generators (see Fig. 19) do not need to turn at 3600 RPM to generate 60-Hz electricity. For example, an 8-pole generator needs to rotate at only 900 RPM. Still, that is very fast compared to the rotation rate of the turbine itself, which may be in the range of 20 to 100 RPM (depending upon turbine diameter). Transmissions are used to convert the low RPM of the turbine to the higher RPM required by the generator. Still, the generator operates on the slip principle—the rotor turns faster than the magnetic field, always adding energy to the power line.

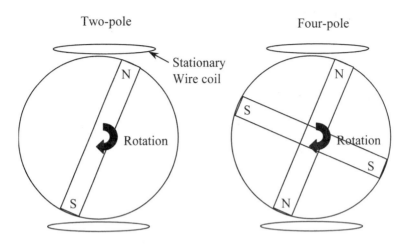

Figure 19: The rotation of an electromagnet in a motor or generator.

The current-carrying coils that produce the magnetic field in the rotor are not shown. On the right is a four-pole magnet. In a generator, the voltage is induced in the stationary wire coils. The slower the rotation rate, the greater the number of poles required to produce the desired voltage.

In a simple induction system, the kind of system used by most early wind turbine, the turbine always had to turn at some fixed RPM. The RPM adjustment would be done by varying the pitch of the blades. That is, if the RPM were to increase, the frequency of the generated electricity would increase. In an early system in Hawaii, when the winds were strong, the utility had to fire up a local diesel generator in order to provide the current for the magnetic fields[30] of the wind farm. After the wind farm was required to pay for that service, they were no longer able to stay in business.

In some more modern induction-generator systems, it is possible to vary the RPM of the turbine by varying the amount of slip. An optical signal is sent to an electronic circuit on the rotating shaft that causes it to adjust the slip to compensate for varying wind speed. It is actually easier to adjust the slip electronically than to adjust the turbine's RPM mechanically.

Modern General Electric wind turbines have rotating magnetic fields, some powered by induction from the power line at 60 Hz, and others are powered by computer-controlled oscillator. The result is magnetic fields

---

[30] In engineering jargon, the induction motors "suck up VARS" (volt-ampere, reactive). The magnetic energy in the coils is immediately returned to the power line, but there are power losses nevertheless.

that rotate at a fixed rate so as to generate 60-Hz electricity, independently of the RPM of the rotor.

In all of these cases except for DC generation, the power line itself is used to produce the magnetic field. By itself, the generator is incapable of generating voltage. Moreover, since it is an alternating-current system, the voltage must be continuously applied. If there is no power on the power line to begin with, the wind turbine is incapable of producing any power.

Words from the PM

Although general physics books often describe generators in terms of permanent magnets (PMs) that move past coils of wire, there are many practical reasons that such generators have not been used. Recent developments, however, have made permanent-magnet generators practical. Especially, we can make large, strong, durable magnets (made with rare-earth metals) that can maintain their magnetic fields despite physical vibrations and years of use.

Usually, a gear mechanism is necessary to convert the slow RPM of the turbine to a high RPM necessary for an ordinary generator to work well. The gear box is actually the most vexing problem to wind-machine engineers. Unlike automobile transmissions, which reduce the high rotation rate of the engine to a low rotation rate of the wheels, wind-turbine transmissions must transform the low rotation rate of the rotor to a high rotation rate required in the generator. High-quality permanent magnets allow us to get rid of the gear box.

As we have seen in Fig. 19, the more magnetic poles there are, the slower can be the rotation. The array of magnets around the periphery of the rotor in Fig. 20, however, allows for the generator to be driven directly. Stationary coils experience a rapidly changing magnetic field, which induces a voltage. The faster the change, the higher the voltage. Most ordinary generators have either one north-south pair or two north-south pairs of electro-magnetic poles. The large array of permanent magnets in Fig. 20 allows for a low-RPM rotation of the rotor to move the magnets past the coils rapidly even at low RPM. Therefore, the rotor can spin at the same lumbering rate as the wind turbine and no gearing is necessary.

General Electric has just announced the purchase of ScanWind, which offers an off-shore 3.5-MW wind turbine featuring direct drive, requiring no transmission. The generator has rare-earth permanent magnets. These units are heavier and about 20% more expensive than the conventional turbines (largely because of the inverter), but there is considerable savings in not having to do expensive repairs out in the water.

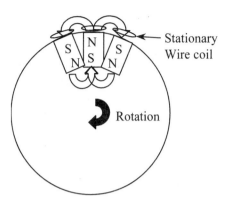

Figure 20: A permanent-magnet generator with numerous permanent magnets around the periphery of a rotor.

Only a few magnets are shown. The curved arrows show the direction of the magnetic field. The motion of the magnets past the coils through each stationary coil induces a voltage.

In such systems, the usual practice is to generate DC voltage and then use an inverter to match the voltage and frequency to those of the power line.

Maintenance

Wind turbines are high-maintenance machines. On a recent trip to Altamont Pass, I saw that most of the wind turbines were spinning; however there were numerous exceptions. Perhaps 80% to 90% of the horizontal axis machines were at work, but the vertical-axis turbines (Fig. 21) were overwhelmingly *not* spinning.

A frequently heard argument in favor of wind energy is that it creates jobs. For that matter, getting rid of heavy machinery at coal mines, and replacing it with men with picks and shovels, would also create jobs in the energy industry. But doing so would be very counter-productive. Cheap energy creates jobs. Anything that increases the cost of energy destroys jobs.

Figure 21: Vertical-axis wind turbines at Altamont Pass.

In July, 2001, under windy conditions, most of them were *not* rotating.

One problem that besets wind turbines in some locations is the buildup of ice on the blades. Of course, that happens only where there are ice storms, namely, in most of the US. It doesn't take much of an imbalance to cause violent shaking of the entire structure. Automatic controls can presumably shut the wind turbine down under such conditions. At the present time, according to *Photonics Tech Briefs* magazine, NASA, MIT, and Visidine are engineering an infrared sensor to detect icing on helicopter blades, which suffer the same kinds of problems as do wind turbine blades.

Yet another problem, for some places at some times of the year, is the presence of dead bugs on the turbine blades. High efficiency requires that the blades be smooth, but the dead bugs roughen the edges.[31] European scientists have discovered that a bug buildup of a millimeter or two on the leading edges of turbine blades can reduce power by as much as 25%.

Safety

It is often advertised that wind turbines are safe, and that they leave most of the land available for crop production. Figure 22 shows one of several collapsed towers I saw from the Altamont Pass Road in July of 2001. I don't imagine that Altamont Pass was a pleasant place to be on the day(s) that the towers keeled over. Nor would I like to be an insurance agent for a wind farm that has kids running around getting into mischief.

---

[31] Yahoo News, 7/04/2001

There is probably more hazard associated with numerous small wind turbines than with large wind farms. That is, one thousand 1-kW_e turbines are more likely to inflict injury than a single 1-MW_e turbine. In a recent windstorm in Southern Colorado, several wind turbines of the 1-kW_e class were destroyed by the wind[32]. These wind turbines were for home and farm use, and were therefore located close to people.

One design problem for wind turbine engineers is that anything that rotates has the same peculiar properties as a gyroscope. For example, a wind turbine might be rotating because of a wind from the east. If the wind direction changes so that the wind comes from the southeast, then there will be an upward or downward twist (depending upon the direction of rotation) on the assembly that holds the wind turbine on the tower.

There was a recent case of a death of a workman in Hawaii due to the dreaded LOBA—Loss-Of-Blade Accident.[33] Whether the LOBA was due to the gyroscope effect or to some other cause, the point remains that the workman was killed.

In some locations raptors, including American Bald Eagles, have been killed in large numbers by wind turbines operating normally. In the Appalachians, there has been considerable bat mortality.

---

[32] Information provided by a local vendor of wind turbines.
[33] Alan S. Lloyd, Professional Engineer, private communication, 11/13/01.

Figure 22: Collapsed wind turbine at Altamont Pass.

The specifications for a certain 600-kW$_e$ wind turbine on the market are worthy of study. It has a diameter of 44 meters (144 feet), and produces its rated output at 28 RPM. At that rate of rotation, the tips of the blades are moving at 64.5 m/s, which is 145 miles per hour. The large 3.6-MW unit made by GE lumbers along at a low rotation rate of 8.5 to 15.3 revolutions per minute. The tips of the blades (110 meter diameter) move at speeds between 49 m/s and 88 m/s (110 mph to 196 mph). No wonder some spokesperson for the Sierra Club has dubbed them *Cuisinarts of the Air*.[34]

Transmission Lines for Wind Farms

The generators themselves produce voltage at somewhere between 480 volts and 4800 volts, and a transformer at the base of the tower raises the voltage to either 12.47 kV or 24.9 kV (in Colorado, at least). The transmission lines that carry the power are underground to protect them from the turbine blades. In a wind farm, the transmission lines form a grid of some layout that depends upon the number of turbines and the overall arrangement of turbines. Regardless of how it is done, some cables have to carry the current from numerous turbines.

Let us consider power loss in line connecting wind turbines spaced in one line. For example, assume that ten 1-MWe generators are tied in series by one-ohm power lines. The power from a 1-MWe turbine (#1) is delivered at 25-kV by a one-ohm cable to the next turbine (#2). The power loss in that one line would be a negligible 1600 watts. The transmission line between turbines #2 and #3 would be 6400 watts. Between #3 and #4, the power loss would be 14.4 kW_e, and so on. The one-ohm power line after #10 would have a power loss of 160,000 kW_e. The power losses add up to about 600,000 watts, which is 6% of the power generated. But a 1000-MW_e wind farm would require 1000 1-MW_e generators, not a mere 10.

This situation is considerably different from that of a large power station that generates 1000 MW_e in one location. No matter what the layout of wind turbines, the problem of keeping power losses within reason amounts to using the highest voltages possible, consistent with underground power lines, and laying out a grid work that keeps wires from becoming overloaded.

Aesthetics

We are accustomed to seeing high-voltage transmission lines, and we are all aware that citizens object to them on some occasions, largely for reasons of aesthetics. Wind farms have also been opposed—in Denmark, England, Australia, and Minnesota, to name a few places—mainly on grounds of aesthetics.

The large wind turbines—500 kW_e and up—dwarf the towers used for high-voltage transmission. But unlike transmission lines that cut a swath

---

[34] Michael Fumento, "Good News, Bad News," *Reason*, (June, 2000). (The Sierra Club has recanted the description.)

that extends for miles, wind farms cover wide areas, miles in *both* directions. In some places, pressure from environmentalists has forced utilities to run their transmission lines underground, at horrendous expense. The aesthetic arguments against transmission lines apply even more strongly to wind turbines. There are some groups who actively oppose industrial wind farms (though many support the use of small wind turbines for homes). Often, it is a Not-In-My-Back-Yard (NIMBY) complaint, such as the following.

> "We have recently reorganized and, thanks to the fact that some of the wealthiest and most powerful people in the world have homes on Cape Cod, are attracting wide and well-funded support. For more, visit:- http://www.saveoursound.-org/getin.html.

> "I predict we are going to become the case study for the wind industry in terms of where NOT to site a wind power plant."

> John Donelan, Associate Director,
> Alliance to Protect Nantucket Sound
> "The Week That Was July 27, 2002," www.sepp.org

The Glass Circus Tent

Picture this. Somewhere in Australia they build a glass circus tent that is 5 kilometers (three miles) in diameter. In the center is a gigantic chimney, twice as tall as the tallest building on earth, at one kilometer (about 3,300 feet) in height. In the hot Australian sun, the land under the glass would heat up. The hot air would move toward the chimney, creating a wind. Some 32 huge wind turbines ("*small* (6.5 MW) turbines", according to the Australian government[35], emphasis added) would tap the energy of the wind and produce 200 megawatts at the hottest time of the day, and a whopping 57 or 80 megawatts on the average, depending upon which reference you believe.[35,36]

Now imagine five of these installations. That's the plan. But why stop there? A mere dozen (or eighteen if the 57-MW figure is correct) will produce as much energy in a year as one nuke situated on a few-acre site.

---

[35] http://www.aie.org.au/pubs/enviromission.htm Thanks to Peter MacSporran of Main Ridge, Australia for calling this project to our attention.

[36] http://www.wired.com/news/technology/0,1282,46814,00.html

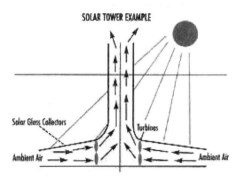

Figure 23: Australian Glass Circus Tent (not to scale).

The diameter would be five kilometers and the chimney height would be one km. Thirty-two wind turbines would produce 200 MW *peak*; about 80 (or 57) MW on the average.

Wind has a complex pattern as it blows through a city, but it always has its highest velocity in the caverns between buildings. That is, to squeeze the same air through a narrower channel requires a higher velocity in the channel. Sander Mertens[37] shows an artist's conception of a pair of sleek, tall, curved buildings joined by an equally sleek bracket that houses three wind turbines. He concedes that the aerodynamic efficiency isn't very good (don't look for numbers in the Renewable Energy magazine *REfocus*), but he finds that a turbine placed within a flat building is better. He says[37] "As a second option locating 'in a duct through the building [such as shown in Fig. 24] is promising."

A 30-meter diameter wind turbine with a duct that extends 20 meters through the building would occupy about 14,000 cubic meters and make a few thousand extra cubic meters unusable as office space. It would produce in the vicinity of 250,000 kWh per year, worth about $25,000 on the retail market.

If the same space were devoted to offices, at least 500 people could be housed. The lowest-paid janitors would probably earn $15,000 per year, and all others would earn more. The businesses would obviously generate more money than they pay in salaries. In other words, the space is worth thousands of times more as office space than as electrical generating space.

---

[37] Sander Mertens, "Wind energy in urban areas: Concentrator effects for wind turbines close to buildings," *Refocus* (March/April 2002).

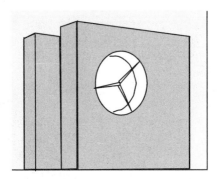

Figure 24: A building-enclosed wind turbine.[37]

Small is Beautiful

Since E.F. Schumacher's 1973 publication of *Small is Beautiful: Economics as if People Mattered,* the title has become something of a mantra to those who imagine that an industrialized giant that has to provide nearly 300 million people with food, water, electricity, roads, heat, sewage treatment, and health care can be operated in the *small* economics mode. See Fig. 25 to see what a piddling 1.5 MW of intermittent wind power looks like.

Figure 25: "Small is Beautiful".

Upper: A man working on a GE 1.5-MW turbine. Photograph courtesy of Sandia National Laboratories, http://www.nrel.gov/data-/pix/searchpix.html; Lower: The base of a 1.5-MW wind-turbine tower (Lamar, CO), and another 1.5-MW turbine in background.

Power Quality

The electricity produced by steam turbines, whether the energy that produces the steam comes from coal, oil, natural gas, or nuclear fission, is of very high quality, because the rotation rate of the generators is nearly constant. Generators turned by diesel engines, by contrast, rotate slightly non-uniformly because of the periodic push of the pistons. The effect can be observed in the power put onto the transmission lines, showing up as overtones of the normal 60-Hz of the power lines. In fact, since the entire grid is tuned to handle 60-Hz power, all of the power in the overtones is eventually lost to heat.

Wind power, according to utility engineers who have to work with it, is the lowest quality power on the planet. The problems are of no particular concern for the rural homeowner, but they are very burdensome to utilities that are required to deliver high-quality power to their customers. One effect is periodic pulsing in the electrical power occasioned by the passage of turbine blades through the "shadow area" of the tower; some wind turbines operate with the turbine blades on the leeward side of the tower.

The Engineers Chase Frequency

When a large load is connected to the power line, the voltage drops, but the more evident change is a drop in the rotation rate of the generators. Electronic sensors immediately detect the resulting decrease in the frequency of the AC electricity. Similarly, when a large load is disconnected from the power line, the frequency increases. A change in frequency is simply the fastest and easiest thing to detect to tell that some changes must be made to the power fed to the grid.

Sudden changes in load are not the only ways to cause fluctuations in line frequency. The same sort of thing can happen when a given power plant suddenly comes on line or goes dead. Suppose that the largest power plant on the line suddenly goes dead for some reason. There must be enough "spinning reserve"—power producing machinery that is already spinning—ready to take up the slack. Normally, the spinning reserve is actually contributing power to the line. If there is a sudden decrease in load—or a sudden increase in wind power, say—the spinning reserve must *reduce* power output. If there is a sudden increase in load—or a sudden decrease in wind power—the spinning reserve must quickly start supplying more power.

Dispatchers at control stations are the hapless souls who must make whatever changes are necessary to return the grid to normalcy. When the grid voltage is erratic, their jobs become as taxing as those of air-traffic controllers.

When a wind farm is providing a small fraction of the power on a grid, the spinning reserve is adequate to handle the inevitable fluctuations caused by the gusty nature of wind. The fluctuations are effectively "negative load," meaning that an increase in wind power is equivalent to a decrease in demand, and a decrease in wind power is equivalent to an increase in demand.

When the wind is gusty at a wind farm, the power can fluctuate wildly, and in short order. When the wind system provides a significant fraction of the power on the line, the wild fluctuations cannot be handled by the normal spinning reserve.

The dispatchers get very exasperated "chasing frequency," trying to hold the line frequency constant while the wind causes the input power to fluctuate wildly. They have to call for more or less power from conventional plants to keep up with the whims of the wind. Doing so causes unnecessary wear on the conventional plants.

Dispatchers can compensate for fluctuations in wind power only when the wind farms supply no more than about 10% of the power in a huge grid. In the words of one utility engineer [private communication]:

> "Utilities have the right to control large fluctuating loads (arc furnaces for example) so their other customers aren't impacted. We should also have the right to control fluctuating sources. But, wind turbines are 'green' so when we raise these concerns we are accused of 'impeding' renewable energy."

Again, if wind were a viable power source, utilities would be champing at the bit to use it. Utilities use every technology available to cut their fuel costs; they would gladly use photovoltaics and wind turbines *if* they produced economically.

Let me be a little more specific about that matter. All utilities know the exact cost—down to a fraction of a penny per kilowatt-hour of producing electricity from every individual power plant. When there is an increase in demand, the utility automatically adjusts things to get the cheapest electricity available. When there is a decrease in demand, they automatically turn down their most expensive power plant. Utilities generally have to be *forced* to buy wind power. By contrast, nuclear power plants run full time, generating 19.6 % of utilities' electrical energy (2007). The EIA recognizes (International Energy Outlook 2001) that wind power exists because of subsidies.

> "Wind power in the United States enjoyed substantial growth in 1999, mostly because of the threatened expiration of Federal tax credit for wind production in June 1999 (which has since been extended to the end of 2001 and then to the end of 2003)."

During that that subsidy-favored year of 1999, wind production in the entire US increased from 2,998 million kWh in 1998 to 4,488 million kWh. The increase in average power was therefore 170 MWe, and the average power production from all wind turbines combined in 1999 was about 511 MW_e, about the amount provided by any medium size power plant.

In 2002, the US produced 52 billion kWh from wind, amounting to an around-the-clock average power of about 5,900 MW of on-again, off-again subsidized power.

> "Americans have not been encouraged this year to start a wind farm. A crucial tax credit for wind producers expired at the end of 2003, and *the turbine trade has been hurting ever since.*" [emphasis added]
>
> Jeremiah Creedon[38]

In other words, absent the subsidies, tax benefits, and people willing to pay extra for what they suppose to be "clean energy", no wind farm on the planet could operate in the black.

Environmental Considerations

The main complaints at this stage have come from bird lovers who have complained about dead birds, chiefly large raptors. Golden Eagles, for one, have been killed by the rapidly moving blades of wind turbines. Other complaints have been about noise (sound), ground vibrations (from large, low-RPM machinery), shadow flicker, and TV interference. Some people have complained that the wind turbines are ugly. Aside from the physical hazard to raptors (and anything that gets in the way when a wind turbine flies apart), these problems could not be considered environmental.

But things have just begun. Wind provides only 1.3% of our electricity. Presumably, the fraction will grow, as Washington's largess continues. But growth in the wind sector is inherently limited by wind's unpredictable nature on all time scales. The Danish experience shows that, even with reliable hydropower to keep the grid steady while the wind varies, the grid can stand only about 10 percent of its power to come from wind.

The scenes at Altamont Pass (See Fig. 17, which shows only a tiny fraction of the wind farm) would be repeated endlessly. How well would wind turbines be accepted in places where they have strong ocean breezes— for example, on the Monterey Peninsula?

---

[38] Jeremiah Creedon, "Increase Your Energy IQ: The more you know about green energy, the more you'll save," *Utne magazine* July / August 2004, http://www.-utne.com/pub/2004_124/promo/11273-1.html

Arguably, these are not serious environmental problems in and of themselves. But small environmental significance has not stopped lawsuits in the past. Nor, one expects, will it in the future.

It's a pity, perhaps, because, aside from hydro and biomass, wind is the best solar prospect.

Chapter 10   Heat Engines & Their Cousins

We can convert electricity to mechanical energy using motors, which are often very efficient. We can convert mechanical energy to electrical energy, using generators, which are usually very efficient. Similarly, we can raise water efficiently, and convert the potential energy of raised water into mechanical or electrical energy very efficiently.

But heat is a different matter. Work can always produce heat, but getting heat to produce work is not always so easy, and it is usually inefficient. In other words, there is an inherent asymmetry that makes heat energy different from other forms of energy. So the subject of heat requires a special discussion.

In this chapter, we will discuss heat *engines*, refrigerators, and heat *pumps*. All of them play a role in our daily lives. Fortunately, all of them can be represented by variations on a simple diagram.

The Generic Heat Machine

Steam engines, gasoline engines, steam turbines, diesel engines, and gas turbines differ considerably in the way they operate, yet they have some common bonds. In every case, heat energy is converted to do useful work; they are all *heat engines*. Also in every case, "waste" heat goes out into the environment.

The schematic representation of the flow of energy in a heat engine is shown in Fig. 26. The high-temperature reservoir is a source of heat. In the case of an automobile engine, combustion of gasoline provides the heat. The low-temperature reservoir is the environment, typically the atmosphere or a body of water. The automobile's exhaust system and radiator both discharge heat into the air.

Of interest, of course, is that the engine actually does something useful called *work*.

It may not be obvious that (in Fig. 26) the heat input Q_{hi} equals the sum of the heat output Q_{low} plus the work W, because people have used different units for heat (calories and BTUs) than for work (foot-pounds, ergs, joules, kilowatt-hours …). But if one city block is measured in feet and the next one in meters, the total length of the blocks is still the sum of the two lengths. We simply have to express both lengths in the same unit.

Similarly, we have to express both heat and work in the same units. If you open up a college textbook on this subject and find the chapter where these heat engines are discussed, you'll find that the problems at the end of the chapter are almost exclusively based on converting units. The physics itself is *very simple*. We simply take the difference between Q_{hi} and Q_{low} to get the work accomplished:

$$W = Q_{hi} - Q_{low} \qquad (1)$$

We will use the *joule* as the unit of energy. Doing so simplifies everything.

Figure 27 shows energy flows with arrows of different widths to represent different magnitudes. Of the three, W is the smallest. Typically the work done is 25% to 40% of the heat input. By implication, the heat output—the "waste heat" rejected to the environment—is 60% to 75% of the heat input. Most of the input heat is "wasted," discharged into the environment.

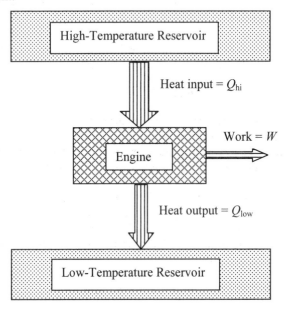

Figure 26:   Energy flow in a heat engine.

Note that $W = Q_{hi} - Q_{low}$, the work done is equal to the difference between the heat input and the heat output.

Efficiency of a heat engine

The purpose of a heat engine is to accomplish work. Therefore, we define its efficiency as the ratio of the work done to the heat input:

$$efficiency = \frac{W}{Q_{hi}} \qquad (2)$$

It is beyond the scope of this discussion to do the full mathematical treatment, but some generalities can be stated about how the efficiency depends upon temperature. Generally the higher the temperature of the high-temperature reservoir and the lower the temperature of the low-temperature reservoir the higher will be the efficiency. That is, high efficiency comes from a large temperature difference with a cold reservoir in which to dump waste heat.

Schematically, we would represent this by the widths of the arrows in Fig. 27. An inefficient engine would be represented by a thin arrow to represent work, as shown in Fig. 27.

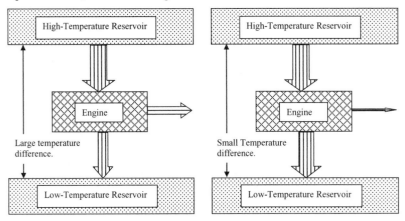

Figure 27:   Energy Flow diagrams for high-efficiency engine (left) and low-efficiency engine (right).

The larger the temperature difference between the reservoirs, the higher is the maximum theoretical efficiency.

Refrigerators and Air Conditioners

Shortly, we will use an energy-flow drawing similar to Fig. 26 to describe the heat and work involved in a refrigerator. But first, we need to discuss how a refrigerator actually works.

Refrigerators have a "working fluid" that remains in the machine. Among the ones in common use are ammonia (not the cleaning liquid, but the gas NH_3), Freon (aka R-12, now banned by the Montreal Protocol), and hydrofluorocarbons R-22 and R-134a. Under modest pressure, they are liquids. Under lower pressure, they evaporate into gases, cooling their surroundings as they evaporate.

Because the parts are available to see, let us look at the air conditioner in a car (Fig. 28). There is a compressor that is turned by a belt. As it turns, it compresses the refrigerant (R-134a, at this date) into a hot gas. The hot gas goes into the heat exchanger in front of the car's radiator where it is cooled by the flow of air. With enough cooling, the refrigerant becomes liquefied.

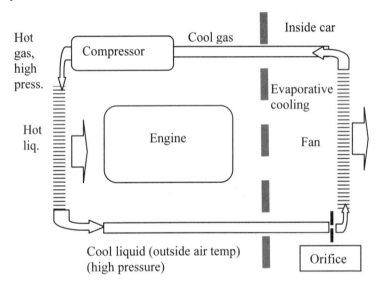

Figure 28: A simplified automotive air-conditioning system

The liquid refrigerant then flows through a small orifice into an expansion chamber located under the dashboard. The expansion chamber is at low pressure because it is continuously being evacuated ("sucked out") by the compressor. As the refrigerant enters this chamber, it evaporates into a gas, taking heat from the metal around it to do so. The expansion chamber is a bit like a radiator in that air is blown through it to cool the inside of the car.

Once the refrigerant has evaporated and warmed by the air that it cools, it is drawn into the compressor for another round.

We see some characteristics of a heat engine here. There is some work done, but it is done *on* the compressor by the engine, via the drive belt. There is heat exchange both at high temperature and at low temperature. Effectively, the air conditioner uses input work to draw heat out of a low temperature reservoir and to discharge it into a high temperature reservoir.

Figure 29 shows the energy flow. Work W causes heat Q_{low} to be withdrawn from the low-temperature reservoir. That much heat, plus the heat produced by the work combine to equal the heat Q_{hi} rejected into the high-temperature reservoir.

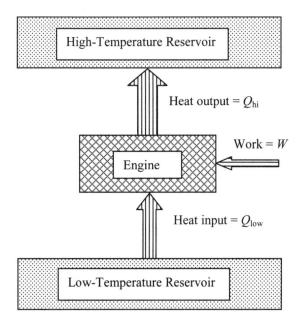

Figure 29: A heat engine run backwards to transfer heat from a low temperature reservoir to a high-temperature reservoir.

Compare the arrow directions with those in Figs. 26 and 27.

Again, the low-temperature reservoir is the interior of the car. That may seem odd when the car has been sitting in the sun and getting very much hotter than the outside world, but the "high" and "low" temperatures refer to the relationship within the system.

It would seem reasonable to use the term *efficiency* for refrigeration systems, defined as the ratio of the heat delivered (in the case of refrigeration or air-conditioning, extracted) to the energy put into the motor that does the work. However, the convention is to use a different term called the *coefficient of performance* (*COP*). Commonly, the *COP* is greater than one ($COP > 1.0$), and all the more so when the environment is cool.

$$COP_{cooling} = \frac{Q_{low}}{W} \qquad (3)$$

The government has introduced a standard misleadingly called the Energy Efficiency Ratio (*EER*) that all manufacturers must measure under standard conditions and display prominently on their air conditioners. By definition, a ratio of two quantities tells how many times the first goes into the second; the *COP* is such a ratio. However, the *EER* is defined to be the heat removal rate *in BTU per hour* divided by the power input *in watts*, and the label never says what the units of EER are. Good air conditioners (*EER* = 10 BTU per hour per watt) can remove 10 BTU of heat per hour for every one watt of electrical power put into the compressor under those circumstances. However, since 3.4 BTU/hr equals 1 watt, the *COP* is 10/3.4 = 2.9. The meaning of *COP* = 2.9 is that every unit of energy put into the air conditioner removes 2.9 units of heat energy from the house.

There is, however, no such thing as *the EER* of an air conditioner, because the ambient temperature has a strong effect on it. Therefore the government now requires manufacturers to display the *seasonal average EER* (*SEER*), still in those arcane units. Divide their number by 3.4 to get the *COP*.

$$COP = \frac{EER \text{ (arcane units)}}{3.4} \qquad (4)$$

Heat Pumps

The only difference between a refrigerator and a heat pump is the purpose. Refrigerators and air conditioners are built for extracting heat from, and therefore cooling, something. A heat pump is used for heating. But the very same machinery can be used for either purpose.

Now consider the heat pump. The upper reservoir in Fig. 29 receives the heat energy extracted from the lower reservoir *plus* the energy (work) that is put in to operate the machine. For example, if one unit of work draws 3 units of energy from the low reservoir (the outside air, or the ground), then 4 units of heat energy is pumped into the upper reservoir (the interior of the house). Note that a *COP* of 3.0 for refrigeration translates to a *COP* of 4.0 for the same device used as a heat pump.

$$COP_{heating} = \frac{Q_{high}}{W} \qquad (5)$$

If you heat your house with electric heaters, one unit of electrical energy produces one unit of heat energy. If you heat with a heat pump, one unit of electrical energy begets 3 to 6 units of heat energy. The actual *COP* depends upon ambient temperature. It is easy to refrigerate when the ambient temperature is low, and easy to heat with a heat pump when the ambient temperature is high. Under these conditions, the *COP* is high. It is hard to refrigerate when the ambient temperature is high and hard to heat when the ambient temperature is low. Then the *COP* is low.

Real Heat Engines

Any machine that uses a fuel or other heat source to produce motion is a heat engine. These include gasoline engines, diesel engines, steam turbines, gas turbines, jet engines, and steam piston engines. The underlying science of efficiency in all such engines has been understood for almost two centuries. Basically, efficiency increases as the temperature difference between the two reservoirs increases, and also as the temperature of the hotter reservoir increases.

Engine efficiency has increased over these two centuries from a few percent to 60 percent, the latter figure applying to combined-cycle power plants. The improvement does not come from better understanding of the underlying physics, but from improvements in technology. Some of the improvement comes from mechanical considerations such as better lubricants, closer tolerances, and wear-resistant metals. In the case of gasoline engines in automobiles, much can be traced to electronics. Continuous readings of the exhaust enable adjustments to fuel supply so as to assure complete burn of the fuel while reducing pollution. But probably most of the improvement has come from materials science, which has produced materials that allow much higher temperatures without concomitant corrosion.

One limitation on the efficiency of automobile engines is that they do not run steadily. The engine speeds up and slows down as speed changes and gearing changes. Similarly, the engines that produce electricity are most efficient when they produce steady power, whereas the ones that respond to sudden increases and decreases in demand have lower efficiency.

The combined-cycle (or co-generation) power plant is a case in point. It has a gas turbine, very much like the jet engine used in aircraft. The turbine blades, where all the heat is generated, are made of single-crystal titanium or of ceramic-coated steel. Either way, the blades can withstand very high temperatures. Nevertheless, the efficiency of the turbine by itself is not spectacular, because the exhaust is very hot. (The temperature of the low-temperature reservoir is high.)

The heat in the exhaust is not thrown away. It is channeled toward a heat exchanger that heats water (with some extra heat from burning some more natural gas) to run a conventional steam cycle. Over all, this combination of a high-temperature gas turbine and a conventional steam cycle has an efficiency of about 60 percent. Such units are used for "base load," the night-and-day demand that never goes away.

Combined Heat and Power (CHP)

Considering Figs. 26 and 27, it is clear that efficiency is limited by the fact that engines need to discard heat into the low-temperature reservoir. Wouldn't it be nice if that "waste' heat could actually be used? After all, it amounts to perhaps 60 to 80 percent of the energy that came from the heat source.

Historically engineers have worked hard to make engine efficiency as high as possible, and that means discarding waste heat at the lowest possible temperature. For that reason, the waste heat comes at a temperature as close to ambient temperature as reasonably possible. That is, the waste heat is not useful for a great number of applications. For example, spent steam emerges from a steam turbine into a pipe at a pressure considerably lower than atmospheric pressure, and at a temperature that most people would find too low for taking a shower. A further problem is that steam engines are usually at electrical power stations that are remote from customers who might benefit from a supply of a low-temperature heat.

All that being said, Denmark has 16 large combined heat-and-power stations that (during winter) use up to 90 percent of the energy in coal. There are about 600 smaller ones, all built recently. In the warmer seasons, of course, there is little need for the waste heat. Curiously, there is an adverse interaction with Danish wind farms. When wind power is high, there is less need for power from the CHP units. But in winter, there is certainly need for the heat from them. So at those times, the wind-generated electricity is sold to other countries at bargain-basement prices.

Production of Electricity

Generators are devices that convert mechanical energy into electrical energy. For the most part, we may ignore the internal details. We simply rotate the shaft and the device produces electricity.

Hiding behind that simplicity is that the more electrical power we use, the more mechanical power we have to supply to the generator. It is very easy to turn a generator and make the voltmeter say (say) 115 volts if the generator is not connected to a load. It is much harder to turn that same generator to make it produce the same 115 volts while powering some light bulbs.

Generators used at electrical power plants are very efficient. They convert roughly 98 percent of the mechanical energy into electrical energy. Engineers are constantly at work trying to increase efficiency by another 0.1%, but for our purposes, those differences are unimportant.

The main efficiency consideration in power plants is in the conversion of heat to work. Whether one uses coal, oil, natural gas, nuclear fuel, geothermal heat, or solar heat, the heat must be converted into mechanical energy to rotate the shaft of a generator. When all electrical generating units in the US are considered together, they convert 33.7% of the primary energy from fuels into electrical energy (2007 figures).

It is often written that the grid is inefficient, and that some 70 percent (say) of the electricity is lost in transmission. These claims are given in order to support the notion of decentralized power. However, the claims are false. The writers confuse heat-to-work losses discussed above with transmission losses.

There are indeed losses in conveying the electricity from the power plants to the customers, but the national average is 7 percent. Overall, 31.55 percent of energy consumed from fuels at the power plants reaches the customer, and by far the lion's share of the loss is the unavoidable loss in converting work to heat.

Chapter 11   Direct Solar Heat

Despite what we occasionally read in the papers about solar homes, they are few and far between. The Energy Information Administration (*Annual Energy Review 2008*) reports a diminution of solar-heated houses since 1985 and 1987, when there were 0.05 million such homes. In the 1999-2007 period, there were 0.02 million solar homes. In the interests of clarity, we are not talking about the number of *new* solar homes, but the number of occupied dwellings.

The Greenhouse Effect

The usual explanation for the greenhouse effect is overly simplistic, especially for a solar heat collector that is feeding heat into a house or a hot-water system. Let us look at what happens to solar energy in a solar collector.

The design of a solar-heat collector is simplicity itself. It is merely a box with a glass (sometimes transparent plastic) window facing the sun. Figure 30 shows a typical solar heat collector, and the caption gives the standard explanation: Sunlight goes in, heats the interior, and the window blocks air flow that would cool the interior. Unless the glass is metallized (*low-e*, see "Windows" in Appendix B), it absorbs IR and radiates IR in both directions, as well as reflecting somewhat. The predominant heat-transfer mechanism, until the "greenhouse" becomes intolerably hot, is convection (and in the case of a real greenhouse, evaporation).

To understand what is wrong with the standard explanation, it is only necessary to ask what would happen if a solar heat collector sat in the sunlight all day. Would it continuously get hotter? No, it would heat up to some maximum temperature and then heat up no more. For example, I assembled a crude solar collector—just a well insulated container with a transparent lid) and put in into the bright Pueblo, Colorado, sunlight in early June when the outdoor temperature was 33 °C (92 °F). The interior temperature initially rose rapidly, then more slowly, eventually leveling off at 92 °C (198 °F). Other collectors have similar behavior. If blocking IR were the only mechanism at work, there would be no stopping the inexorable heat rise until the glass melted.

Why doesn't the collector keep getting hotter and hotter? Think of it this way. You have a room with huge windows, and you try to keep the room hot enough to boil water. Obviously, you would have to pour in a lot of heat because there is a lot of heat lost through those windows. The windows block IR, to be sure, but they do also *conduct* heat. Eventually the solar collector reaches an equilibrium temperature where the rate of heat loss through the glass and through the walls exactly equals the rate that heat comes in via sunlight.

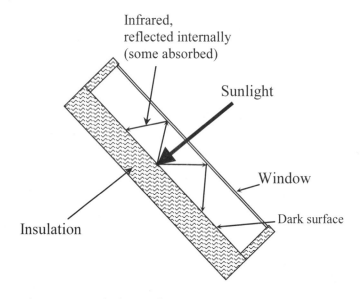

Figure 30: A solar heat collector.

Sunlight passes through the glass and strikes the dark surface, which absorbs the energy and becomes hotter. According to the standard explanation, the surface radiates infrared (IR) radiation, but the window blocks that radiation from leaving. Mostly, however, heat is retained by restricting air flow.

When the the surroundings are colder, the equilibrium temperature of the interior is also lower. The reason is simple. The rate of heat loss is proportional to the temperature difference between the inside and the outside.[39] For example, the collector I tested achieved a temperature (98 °C 198 °F) that was 41 °C (106 °F) above that of the surroundings. On a

---

[39] See Insulation and R-value in Appendix B, page 247.

freezing day (0 °C, 32 °F), the interior temperature could rise only to 41 °C (138 °F).

And, what was the efficiency of my solar collector when it reached 92 °C? A big fat zero percent. The efficiency is the ratio of the energy delivered (in this case, heat) to the energy input. No energy from the collector was delivered to anything. Zero divided by something is still zero.

If I had built the solar collector so that it could deliver heat to some target (water, or room air, perhaps), the temperature of the collector would drop somewhat, depending upon how fast it was delivering heat. By vigorously moving water through the system, I could achieve an efficiency of about 80 percent. (The glass reflects sunlight to that extent.) That is, if the collector were not allowed to warm up above the temperature of the surroundings, the rate of heat loss would be zero. *All* of the heat collected from the sun would be delivered to the target. (We are ignoring the power used in pumping the water around.)

On a summer day when the temperature is 33 °C (92 °F), most people would be loath to heat their houses with sunlight or anything else. Home heating is something one wants on cold days. If the outdoor temperature were 0 °C, the solar collector could still be made to operate at nearly 80% efficiency. Just circulate enough water (or air) to keep the temperature of the collector above the freezing point. But that's a pretty poor way to heat a house—using freezing air. (I'm told it's an old trick that slumlords use.)

To heat a house usually requires the temperature of the circulating air to be at least 50 °C (120 °F). That is well above the ambient temperature, so it is obvious that the collector will lose heat to the surroundings. Moreover, the temperature of the collector will be above the temperature of the moving air, typically 5 °C or more, meaning that the collector itself would be 55 °C.

Therefore the efficiency will be well short of the maximum 80%. We will use the data from Fig. 31 for a typical commercial collector to find the efficiency under the circumstances given: solar intensity of 950 W/m², 0 °C ambient temperature, 55 °C inside the collector. The efficiency would be 31%.

If the ambient temperature were 10 °C lower, namely −10 °C (14 °F), the collector would still have to be 55 °C, therefore 65 °C above ambient. The efficiency would be 22%. Similarly, if the ambient temperature were 10 °C (50 °F), the efficiency would be 40%. The colder the ambient temperature, the lower the efficiency of the collector. Usually, of course, the colder the ambient temperature, the lower the quantity of available sunlight. This is exactly the opposite of what one would desire.

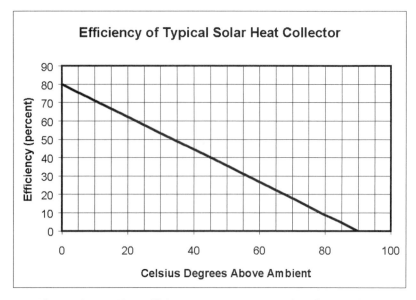

Figure 31:   The efficiency-temperature graph of a typical commercial solar heat collector.

The efficiency is graphed versus the difference between internal and external temperatures. Solar intensity of 950 W/m^2 is assumed.

The sea-level intensity of sunlight is never 950 W/m^2 except in low latitudes when the sky is clear in the summertime. When the sun is blocked by haze, the solar intensity can easily drop by half to 475 W/m^2. Under those circumstances, the efficiency curve looks a bit different. The interior temperature can never rise 90° C above ambient; in fact it will rise at most 45 °C above ambient, as shown in Fig. 32.

To emphasize just what happens when the sunlight is at half-intensity, as shown in Fig. 32, consider the case where the solar collector is 20 °C warmer than the surroundings outdoors. The efficiency would be 63% in full sunlight, but only 45% in half-sunlight. In other words, for every square meter of collector, the solar collector would deliver 63% of 950 Watts (heat) to the house in full sunlight, but 45% of 475 watts at half sunlight. In other words, the collector would only deliver 36% as much heat to the house under the half-sun conditions.

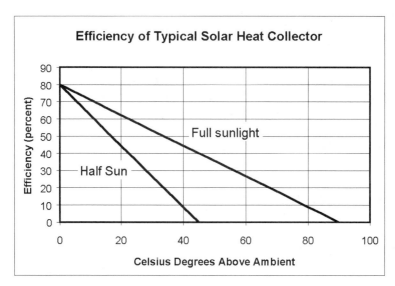

Figure 32: The efficiency-temperature graph of a typical commercial solar heat collector.

The efficiency is plotted versus the difference between internal and external temperatures, shown for solar intensities of 950 W/m² (Full), and 475 W/m² (Half). Note that in this example, if the collector is 20 °C warmer than the environment, the efficiency is about 63% if there is full sunlight, but only 45% in half sunlight.

Beyond that, half-sun conditions are usually (although not always) associated with cooler outdoor air. This increases the temperature difference between the inside and outside of the collector, decreasing the efficiency even further.

The half-sun condition does not need to come from cloudy weather. The angle of the sun's rays depend upon the latitude and the time of day, and that angle has an effect on the intensity. When the sun's rays are 60° from being perpendicular to the surface, the solar intensity is effectively halved.

Avoiding the Expense

Any book on solar home-heating emphasizes the following rule, although not in these exact words.

Rule #1: Insulate your house so well that *even* solar energy can heat it.

Sunday supplements extolling the features of solar homes never fail to explain how the builder installed gobs of insulation. Unfortunately, they always talk about the home as if it were a *solar* home. Invariably, it is a well-insulated home with a standard heating system. The solar collector system is often an expensive add-on that is of little consequence. It is the *insulation*, not the solar collectors, that deserves the lion's share of the credit for decreasing heating bills.

Solar collectors are expensive and usually unsightly. Large windows are expensive and often beautiful. Therefore, the preferred way to use sunlight to heat a home is to install large south-facing windows with a roof overhang that allows winter sunlight in and blocks overhead summer sunlight. This so-called *passive-solar* heating is not included in the EIA's count of solar homes. In fact, probably most of the homes in the US can lay claim to *some* solar heat, if only because sunlight enters windows some time during the day. The EIA's data that a mere 0.02% of the nation's 111 million homes are solar-heated refers only to those homes that have external solar collectors.

Some homes built according to this model have large masses of stone (or water) that warm up in the sunlight and release heat at night. They have the double virtue of storing heat for the night and keeping the house from getting *too* hot during the day.

The disadvantage of passive solar is that windows are not nearly as good at retaining heat as insulated walls are. A fiberglass-insulated stud wall is about 5 times as good an insulator as a double-pane window of the same area. Therefore, it is necessary to install heavy curtains or other insulation to keep heat from escaping at night.

Heating the Pool

Heating swimming pools in the summer is an entirely different matter from heating homes in the winter. Plenty of sunlight is available, the storage system is the water itself, and the collector never needs to be hot.

Imagine a serpentine array of black PVC pipe on a south-facing roof as shown in Fig. 33. There is no glass to reflect any light, so the efficiency is not limited to 80% as it is with typical glazed collectors. Figure 34 shows the performance of a commercial solar heat collector for a swimming pool. The light line is for a typical solar collector for home heating. The heavy line is for a commercial solar heater for swimming pools. When the temperature of the collector is not far above that of the surroundings, the efficiency of the collector can approach 90%.

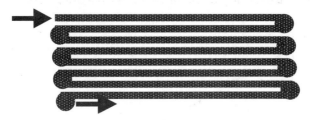

Figure 33: A primitive solar swimming pool heater.

There is a serpentine array of black plastic pipe on a south-facing roof. The water from the swimming pool is pumped through the system, heating the water and cooling the collector. The collector never gets hot enough to lose much heat to the surroundings; therefore the efficiency is very high.

The solar collector for heating swimming pools thus satisfies several important criteria: low cost, high efficiency, and simplicity. It wins no points in a beauty contest.

In arid climates, the most important mechanism that cools swimming pools is evaporation. Simply covering the pool with a clear plastic sheet has the dual advantage of limiting evaporation and letting sunlight in to heat the pool.

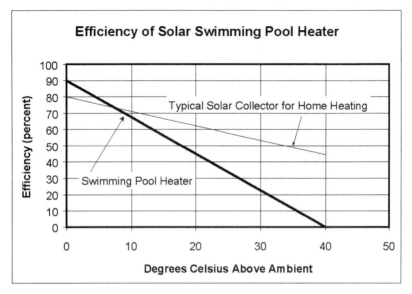

Figure 34: Comparison between typical solar home heater and swimming pool heater.

The efficiency curve for a commercial swimming pool solar heat collector (heavy line) compared to a typical solar collector for home heating (light line). When the pool heater is only slightly warmer than its surroundings, its efficiency approaches 90 percent.

Curiously, solar swimming-pool heaters are a poor seller in Hawaii. The reason is that heat pumps consume less electricity than the water pumps necessary to use solar energy for the same job.[40]

Domestic Hot Water

Using sunlight to heat domestic water up to the temperature required for a dishwasher is necessarily inefficient, just as Fig. 31 suggests. However, water emerging from pipes in the ground (typically at 10 °C, 50 °F) can be pre-heated efficiently by a solar collector to, say, 38 °C (100 °F), especially in the warmer months. The regular water heater can then finish the job.

---

[40] Alan S. Lloyd, Professional Engineer, private communication 11/13/01.

There are books that tell how to make and install domestic solar water pre-heaters of several designs, and I will not attempt to steal their thunder.

"Kazimir's prize-winning Pacemaker water heater, designed for a household of two, uses existing water tanks, sells for about $700, and can be installed by a non-plumber who is handy with tools. Though it is on sale at several Home Depot outlets, the product has sold better in the Caribbean than in Florida."

Berman & O'Connor (1996)

No doubt the sales of the Kazimir are better in Florida than in Minnesota.

The Market for Solar Heat Collectors

The US Energy Information Agency (EIA)'s *Annual Energy Review,* both in book form and on the web at www.eia.doe.gov, gives data on the shipments of solar collectors, reckoned in thousands of square feet sold, year-by-year. (The EIA data are here converted to square meters.) According to the *Annual Energy Review 2008*, since 1974, about 35 million square meters of solar heat collectors have been "shipped" in the US. The figure evidently includes all shipments within the US, as well as exports and imports.

If all of the solar heat collectors sold in the US from 1979 to 2009 are still in service, the total is 35 million square meters, equivalent to 12.5 square miles. Figure 35 shows the annual shipments of solar thermal collectors from 1987 till 2007. High-temperature thermal units (the right-hand bars in Fig. 35) went off the market after 1990, but enjoyed some momentary resurgence in 2006. The predominant type of solar collector has been the low-temperature type, which are, after all, the most efficient ones.

Not surprisingly, the overwhelming use for solar collectors is the heating of swimming pools. Those heaters constitute 88% of the market (measured in surface area of solar collector). Solar collectors for domestic space heating and for hot water are about 0.7% and 10% of the total market, respectively.

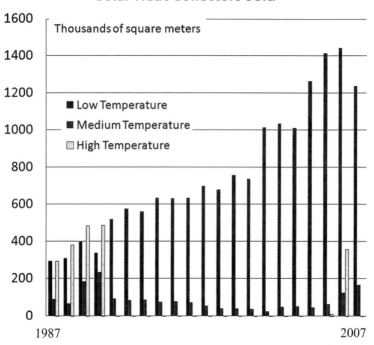

Figure 35: Shipments of solar thermal collectors, in thousands of square meters.

Some 93% of the collector shipments are low-temperature collectors.

It should surprise nobody that the chief buyers of solar-thermal collectors reside in just a few states. See Fig. 36. The top destinations are Florida (51%), California (23%), and Arizona (6.5%).

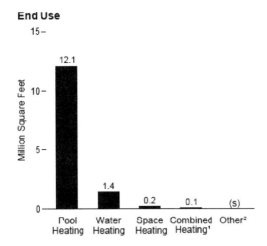

Figure 36: Solar heating units sold in the US (2007), sorted by type.

The quantities are given in millions of square feet (data from *2008 Annual Energy Review*). Multiply by 0.092 to get square meters.

More Sobering Statistics

In the US, 4.3% of our energy is used for heating homes. An additional 2.1% of our energy is used for heating water in homes. Heating of commercial establishments requires 0.2% of our energy, and space- and water-heating in commercial establishments requires another 0.1%. Considered together, heating of the air and water in homes and commercial establishments accounts for 6.7% of our energy consumption. If, by some miracle, we could suddenly get *all* of our domestic and commercial space heating and hot water from sunlight, we would have solved 6.7% of the energy problem.

What about the other 93.3%?

Chapter 12   Electricity from Solar Heat

Benjamin Franklin experimented with electricity, but he had no idea how it might be used. Michael Faraday, asked by a member of the British Parliament what earthly good could come of his research into electricity, replied that he did not know, but that "some day you will tax it."

Electricity is our most versatile form of energy. It can provide light, motion, and the power for all of the ubiquitous electronics that are a part of our daily lives. It is not—presently—well suited to transportation, except for commuter railways in cities like Boston.

Looking at the pattern of energy usage in the US over the past several decades, the most remarkable change is the growth in the electrical energy fraction. In 1975, we used 28.2 percent of our energy to generate electricity, with a heat-to-electricity efficiency of 32.8 percent. By 2007, the efficiency had increased to 34.5 percent, but we also used 40.7 percent of our primary energy to produce electricity. Much of the increase is due to the computer revolution. Not only are computers sitting on every desktop, but the "internet hotels" that route data all over the globe are also gobbling up electrical energy. Another reason for the increase is the widespread use of air-conditioning, which has made places like Florida more habitable.

There is something very appealing about converting sunlight directly to electricity with no moving parts. "Obviously" (it says here), there is nothing to wear out. All we need to do is to put something out in the sunlight and we'll have electricity.

There is nothing particularly new about the concept of converting sunlight to electricity. In 1822, T. S. Seebeck obtained an electric current by heating one of the junctions of a bi-metallic ring, and it was only a matter of time before thermocouples using the Seebeck effect were in use as temperature-measuring devices. Let the source of heat be sunlight, and there's solar electricity, albeit of low efficiency.

Another way to use sunlight to produce electricity is to focus the sun's rays to heat water (directly or indirectly) to a high enough temperature to run a steam engine.

Yet a third way, discovered in 1878, but commercially developed within the last few decades, is to produce electricity directly, without having to produce heat. Everybody these days is familiar with solar-powered calculators, for example. It is this new, somewhat exotic, *photovoltaic* technology that has some people very excited about solar energy for the future. In the view of some, it is an infant technology that will eventually become cheap enough to enjoy widespread use. After all, solar cells are made of silicon, the same stuff that computer chips are made of. "Look how the price has been dropping!" they say. Don't count on it.

Some Solar Installations

There are two major installations in the US devoted to producing electricity from the heat of sunlight. Of course, sunlight has to be concentrated to produce the high temperatures necessary. The installation at Solar Two near Barstow, California, shows one method to accomplish the task, and the parabolic-trough array at Daggett, California, shows another. Both installations are in the best solar location in the US, namely, the Mojave Desert.

Solar Two

In a unit called *Solar Two*, shown in Fig. 37, computer-controlled mirrors reflect light onto a central tower where the concentrated sunlight heats a heat-transfer oil called *therminol*. The hot therminol is pumped to a heat exchanger where the heat is transferred to water to make steam to run an engine. The engine is coupled to a generator to produce electricity.

It is important to understand that magnifying glasses and mirrors *concentrate* light, but *do not create it*. We all learned, as children, how to cause high temperature by focusing the sun's rays into one bright spot.

The installation is called *Solar Two* because *Solar One* burned up in a fire on August 31, 1986 when 240,000 gallons of heat-transfer oil caught fire. The fire did not destroy (most of) the mirrors, however, because they are spread out over a large area. A new tower was constructed, and new experiments were begun.

Carol Browner, the head of the EPA in the Clinton administration, is shown in Fig. 38 giving a pep talk at Solar Two. Little did she know that *Solar Two* would soon become the *Keck Solar Two Observatory*, a research facility no longer dedicated to producing electricity.

Figure 37: Solar Two in the Mojave Desert as seen from the air.

Computer-controlled mirrors direct sunlight to the tower, where the high intensity of light heats oil that in turn heats water to make steam to drive a turbine to produce electricity. Photograph courtesy of http://www.nrel.gov/data/pix/searchpix.html, taken by Joe Flores, Southern California Edison

Notice in Fig. 37 that the shadow area seen beneath the mirrors is a small fraction of the actual land area of the site. Obviously, a lot of sunlight goes unused, and it is of interest to consider why.

Figure 38: Clinton's EPA Head Administrator Carol Browner gives a pep talk at Solar Two.

Photograph courtesy of http://www.nrel.gov/data/pix/searchpix.html, taken by Warren Gretz.

There is much in common here with the problem of being able to see a movie screen in an auditorium where all of the seats are on one flat floor. Somebody's head is always in the way. If the screen is low, the only people who can see it are the ones in the front row; if the screen is raised, the view improves for the ones near the front, but remains bad for those at the rear, until the screen is very high indeed.

Figure 39 shows a two-dimensional sketch (looking south at about 9:00 a.m. in mid-summer) of how the solar mirror assembly works. Light from the sun, now somewhat low on the southeastern horizon, reflects off the mirrors. Each mirror is tilted a bit differently from the others, so that the light will strike the top of the tower.

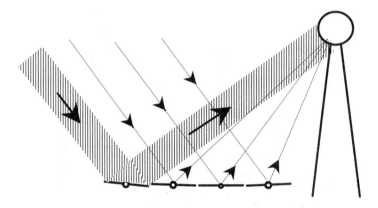

Figure 39: Schematic of sunlight reflecting from an array of mirrors to heat a central tower.

View looking south at about 9:00 a.m. in midsummer.

Figure 40 shows the same mirror assembly at 3:00 p.m. The sunlight comes from the southwest and reflects toward the tower; however, some parts of the mirrors are in the shade. The drawings are exaggerations that make the situation look a lot *better* than it actually is. The distance to the farthest mirror is only a little greater than the height of the tower.

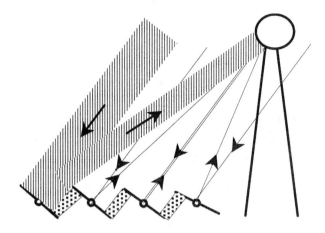

Figure 40: The same array of mirrors as shown in Fig. 39, but at 3:00 p.m. instead.

The dotted area shows that some parts of the mirrors will be in shade, and some reflected light will be blocked by the backside of the nearby mirror.

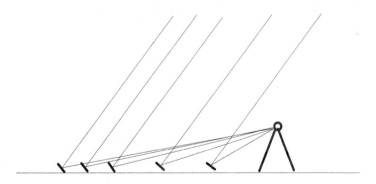

Figure 41: The geometry at Solar Two.

The distance from the tower to the farthest mirrors is about four times the height of the tower, not equal to the height of the tower as shown in Figs. 39 and 40.

In the actual Solar Two installation, the distance to the farthest mirror is about four times the height of the tower, as shown in Fig. 41. Obviously, the mirrors need to be spread out considerably so as to avoid the shading problem. In the aerial photograph (Fig. 37), which shows only a small part of the 130-acre (53-hectare) installation, you can still see that the mirrors become spread out more as the distance from the tower increases.

How About a Bigger Field of Mirrors?

Solar Two is, of course, a demonstration project that is not intended to provide serious amounts of power. But how could it be scaled up? One way would be to double the diameter of the field of mirrors and to double the height of the tower. The mirrors would quadruple the power delivered to the top of the tower. Of course, the tower would have to be twice as tall and would have to carry the additional weight of the larger power-handling equipment. The legs would have to be *more* than four times as strong, not only to carry the additional load, but to provide more rigidity against wind thrust. All in all, then, there is little point in increasing the size. It would probably be just as easy to simply build another entire system, tower, mirrors, and all.

The Solar Two site occupies 52.6 hectares (130 acres) and produces 10 MWe *peak*. Its capacity factor is about 16%. For a Solar-Two installation to produce as much energy as a typical 1000-MWe power plant does in a year, it would have to cover about 33,000 hectares (127 square miles). That is environmental impact!

Parabolic Trough: SEGS (LUZ International)

Not far away from Solar Two, in Kramer Junction, California, there is another solar installation called *SEGS* (Solar Electric Generating System, built by LUZ International), of which there are nine units.[41] SEGS uses an array of parabolic mirrors (see Fig. 43), laid out on north-south axes to concentrate reflected sunlight onto a black tube through which therminol flows. The therminol delivers the heat to a Rankine steam engine whose shaft turns a generator. The SEGS installation has a natural gas boiler and a gas reheater. The purpose of the gas assist is to assure that the steam turbine receives steam at 371 °C regardless of the actual temperature of the therminol in the solar field.

It is a 355-MW installation[42] with 9 separate fields of mirrors in Daggett, Kramer Junction, and Harper Lake, California. Together they

---

[41] Gilbert E. Cohen, David W. Kearney, and Bob G. Cable, "Recent Improvements and Performance Experience at the Kramer Junction SEGS Plants," (www.kjcsolar.com/ASMEF961.html, downloaded 3/9/99).

[42] http://en.wikipedia.org/wiki/Solar_Energy_Generating_Systems

expose 2.273 million square meters of mirror aperture[43] to the sun and produce an average (1998-2002) of 74.7 MW.

Figure 42: The solar-trough array at Kramer Junction, California.

The shiny surfaces focus sunlight onto the black tubes that run along the array. The therminol fluid, thus heated, is pumped to a heat exchanger where it is used to boil water for a (Rankine) steam engine. As the sun moves from east to west, the reflectors rotate so as to keep facing the sun. Photograph taken by the author.

Immediately we can calculate the capacity factor as 74.7/354 = 21.1%. We may also calculate that the mirrors generate an average of 32.8 watts per square meter of aperture.   The land area devoted to the mirrors is approximately twice the aperture area (See Fig. 42), so the field produces about 16 W/m^2 of land area.

However, SEGS is allowed to get 25% of its heat from natural gas, so we can calculate more reasonable numbers for the actual solar production as 15.8% capacity factor and 12 W/m^2 of land area. (The latter figure, we remind, is based on a rough estimate of land area from Fig. 42.)

---

[43] The aperture is the flat area measured across the opening of the parabolic trough.

Figure 43: The solar-trough array at Kramer Junction, California, showing a worker for size comparison.

Photograph courtesy of http://www.nrel.gov/data/pix/searchpix.html, taken by Luz International.

There are three processes at work, each with its own efficiency. The *optical efficiency* varies from 71% (units I and II) to 80% (units VIII and IX). That is, between 71% and 80% of the sunlight that strikes the mirrors is actually reflected to the pipes containing the therminol. They achieve this high efficiency by washing the mirrors every five or so days, and with a high-pressure wash every ten-to-twenty days. Let's repeat that: they wash several million square meters of mirror—much more than the 2.3 million m^2 of aperture—about 25 times a year!

The *thermal efficiency*—that is, the efficiency by which sunlight directed at the oil-containing tubes becomes heat within the system—varies from 35% to about 50%.

The *thermodynamic efficiency*—the efficiency of converting heat to work (thence to produce electricity)—is unspecified in any available literature, but is probably about 35%. One should expect an overall efficiency, therefore, of 71% × 35% × 30% = 8.7% at the minimum to 80% × 50% × 35% = 14% for the best units. That is, about 8.7% of the 2.2 billion watts of sunlight would be 190 MWe (megawatts, electrical); 14% would yield 308 MWe.

In any case, the nine SEGS units together produce about 900 GWh of electricity per year, equivalent to an around-the-clock average output of 103 MWe *with*, we add, the help of the natural-gas backup system to produce power in cloudy weather. Any serious power plant these days delivers about 10 times as much, namely, 1000 megawatts.

To qualify for the tax credits for solar installations, SEGS can use natural gas to supply up to 25% of the energy of the plant, and that's about how much they use. That is, sunlight in the SEGS system produces 75% of the 900 GWh/year produced by the system. This is equivalent to 77 MWe average power, far less than its rated power of 355 MW. The capacity factor of the plant is therefore 77/355 = 22%.

According to the National Renewable Energy Lab (NREL), the productivity of the SEGS system is about 0.5 MWe/hectare (equal to 50 W/m^2),[44] referring to *peak* MWe per unit of land area. With the capacity factor of 22%, this amounts to an around-the-clock average of about 10.8 watts per square meter. To scale that up to the size of a 1000-MWe plant would require 92 square kilometers, or about 33 square miles.

Importantly, SEGS produces its power in midday when it is needed most. As a supplemental source of electricity, units like SEGS can undoubtedly play a role *if* they can get the cost down. Solar energy is free, it is said, but the cost of electricity from SEGS is now about 8–10 cents/kWh. That's the *wholesale* price of course, and the price is that low only because of numerous tax incentives and subsidies.

If the good news is that the SEGS system (using a natural-gas backup system to maintain power) produces a whole 10% as much electricity as one large nuke, the bad news is that the SEGS system's paltry output is *90% of the US's direct solar electricity*.

Fire!

On February 27th, 1999, a tank containing some 900,000 gallons of the therminol caught fire at the SEGS-II unit. The fire was reported in the *Los Angeles Times*. Until SEGS-II was repaired, the power output of the SEGS system as reduced by about 8%.

---

[44] http://www.nrel.gov/documents/profiles.html, "Profiles In Renewable Energy: Case Studies of Successful Utility Sector Projects"

Chapter 13   Nuclear Energy

Before 1945, very few people knew anything about the nucleus of the atom. Picture an atom enlarged so that the orbiting electrons speed around the walls of the room. On that scale, the nucleus is the size of a pinhead. But in terms of mass, it is the other way around. The nucleus has thousands of times as much mass as the orbiting electrons.

Electrons are negatively charged. (The algebraic sign goes back to somebody's arbitrary labeling of the terminals of rudimentary batteries.) Protons are positively charged. That attraction of opposites is what keeps the electrons bound to the atoms. An atom has the same number of electrons as it has protons.

A nucleus may—and always does, with the sole exception of the normal hydrogen nucleus—contain neutrons, uncharged particles of about the same mass as protons. Iron, for example, has 26 protons and (normally) 30 neutrons. But the iron nucleus can also have 28, 31, or 32 neutrons in a stable configuration. Since all chemical properties depend on the electrons, the chemical nature is independent of the number of neutrons.

On the low end of the periodic table, the number of neutrons is nearly equal to the number of protons. Oxygen has 8 protons and 8 neutrons. As the number of protons increases, the number of neutrons increases more than equally. For example, the normal iron nucleus has 4 more neutrons than protons. A common isotope of tungsten—that thin wire in your light bulbs—has 74 protons, but 110 neutrons. Gold has 79 protons, but 118 neutrons. We say that the nuclei on the high end of the periodic table are *neutron rich*.

Reputedly, the nucleus contains massive amounts of energy. But let us put that comment in context. Why do we say that gasoline has a lot of energy? In truth, it has none, in and of itself. Only when the gasoline is burned does it release energy.

Some nuclei, those on the low end of the periodic table, are a bit like gasoline. They cannot release energy without combining with other nuclei in a process we call *fusion*. Two isotopes of hydrogen, ^{2}H (deuterium, one proton plus one neutron in the nucleus) and ^{3}H (tritium, one proton plus two neutrons) can be combined through very complicated processes at extreme temperatures to form helium (He), with the release of several million times as much energy as the same hydrogen releases when burned. The fusion process is the source of the sun's energy.

Nuclei on the high end of the periodic table can release energy by certain kinds of dissociation. In other words, the nucleus comes apart. In many cases, the behavior is spontaneous. For example, radium-226 (^{226}Ra) expels two protons and two neutrons in one bundle called an alpha (α)

particle, and becomes a radon (^{222}Rn). The α emerges with very high energy, on the order of a million times normal chemical energy release per atom involved. This is but one example of *radioactive decay*, the process that keeps the earth's interior supplied with heat.

What would happen if two nuclei on the high end of the periodic table get together? That is a topic of research, to be sure, but of no practical value. Those nuclei have so much positive charge that they repel each other violently, and can be forced together only in extreme accelerators.

Actually, the only things that can penetrate such nuclei are uncharged particles, neutrons in particular. One common process is for the neutron simply to be absorbed by the nucleus, increasing it mass by one unit. A ^{226}Ra might become a ^{227}Ra, for example.

Of special interest is the U-235 (^{235}U) nucleus, which is a rare isotope of uranium. The dominant isotope is U-238. The U-235 component is only 0.7% of all uranium.

When U-235 absorbs a neutron, it becomes U-236, a very unstable nucleus. It breaks into two entirely different atoms in the middle region of the periodic table. The nucleus U-236 is very neutron rich, so in this *fission* process of flying apart, some neutrons are released. Overall, the fission releases about 50 times as much energy as an α decay. See Fig. 44.

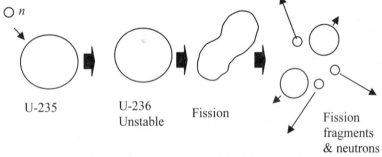

Figure 44: Neutron-induced fission of the U-235 nucleus.

U-235 absorbs a neutron, becoming U-236, which soon flies apart into two nuclei ("fission fragments") and a few neutrons. The fission fragments are the "nuclear waste."

Although we use the term *nuclear energy*, it is a mistake to think that the released energy is something new and mysterious. Nuclear forces hold the nucleus together, but when a charged particle (like an α particle or one of the daughter nuclei in the fission process) becomes dislodged just so far, then it is violently repelled by the remaining nucleus, both being positive. That repulsion is what causes the energy to be so high. In fact, it enabled physicists to estimate the energy release from fission long before anybody was able to measure it. All they needed to know was the amount of charge and the approximate size of the nucleus.

Fission reactors

The United States has 104 nuclear power plants in operation, providing about 20% of our electricity. All of the reactors are *light-water reactors*, for which the fuel is U-235. Normal uranium has been *enriched* by isolating U-235 and making a mixture that contains three-to-five percent U-235, the remainder being U-238. Canadian CANDU reactors can use natural uranium (0.7% U-235), but the water bath is made not of normal H_2O, but of D_2O (D = Deuterium), called *heavy water*. Overall, there are about 400 nuclear power plants in the world, and a large number of nuclear vessels like aircraft carriers plying the seas.

There is a disadvantage to using light-water reactors, namely that they rely on the rare U-235 isotope.

There are ways to take advantage of U-238, and even the more abundant thorium isotope Th-232, but this brief discussion does not have the space. Suffice it to say that the world does not need to rely on that one rare U-235 isotope.

How much uranium is there in the world? There is no meaningful simple answer to that question. If you ask how much elemental uranium metal at 100 percent concentration is there within a few kilometers of the surface, the answer is zero. Uranium is always chemically bound.

You can also ask how much uranium there is in the world at 0.1-percent concentration, or at 0.01-percent concentration. Refer to Figure 45. There is about 3,000 times as much uranium at 0.01-percent concentration as there is at 0.1-percent concentration. There is about 3,000 times as much uranium at 0.001-percent concentration as there is at 0.01-percent concentration. Each time you specify a lower concentration, you get a much larger quantity.

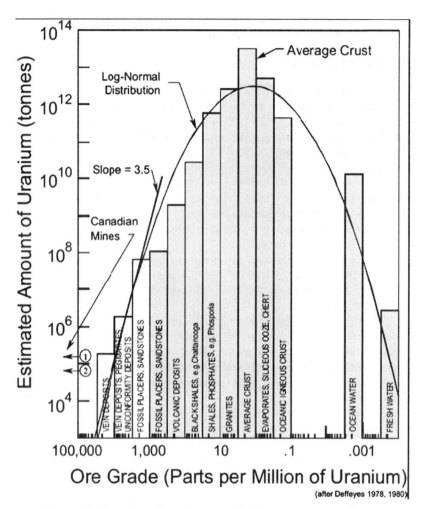

Figure 45: Quantity of uranium, worldwide, versus ore grade.

Highest grade on left. For the steep region (slope=3.5), each time we reduce ore grade by a factor of 10, there is 3,000 times as much uranium in the world. Graph from Erich A. Schneider and William C. Sailor, "Long-Term Uranium Supply Estimates," *Nuclear Technology,* Vol. 162, pp. 379-387 June 2008.

So if we use *all* of the energy in uranium, instead of just the 0.7 percent that is U-235, we can get about 100 times as much energy from a given amount of uranium. But because we can get 100 times as much energy, the inherent value of the uranium increases 100-fold, so we could economically mine uranium at 100 times lower concentration. That gives us 3,000 × 3,000 times as much uranium. Put all that together, and we're talking about 100 × 3,000 × 3,000 = 900 million times as much energy as is available using only U-235 from rich deposits. In other words, if the uranium from rich deposits were adequate to supply the world with all of its energy for only one year, using the (known) technologies to use all of the uranium, instead of just the U-235 fraction, would be adequate to supply the earth for 900 million years.

To summarize, there is no shortage of nuclear energy and there never will be. Nuclear energy is every bit as "renewable" as any other "renewable" source; as we saw in Chapter 5, the important issue is how long the source will last.

Electricity from Nuclear Power

Nuclear fission on the atomic scale may look complicated, but for all practical purposes, it is just a heat source. Heat from combustion of coal, oil, natural gas, wood chips, geothermal sources, and sunlight can be used to produce steam to turn a turbine. Heat from a nuclear reactor does the same.

Figure 46 shows a diagram of a nuclear power plant. The reactor is within the containment building. It produces very hot water under pressure, hence its name: pressurized water reactor (PWR). The steam generator transfers heat from the PRW into water circulating at lower pressure to generate steam, which is piped outside the containment building to the steam turbine.

The steam turbine does not care whether the steam is produced by combustion of fuels, solar heat, geothermal heat, or nuclear fission. That is, all of the power plant outside the containment building is conventional.

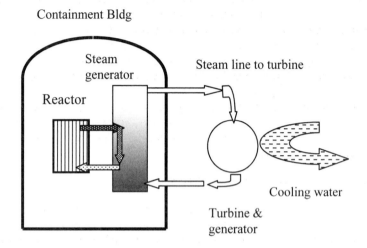

Figure 46: Sketch of a pressurized-water reactor.

Water heated to high temperature and high pressure is produced in the nuclear reactor. That water is pumped to a steam generator where it heats water in a separate loop to produce steam. The steam exits the containment building through pipes to the turbine which spins, producing electricity with a generator. Cooling water is brought in from a lake, river, or a cooling tower.

Radioactive Waste

The nuclei that result when a uranium nucleus breaks apart—so-called *fission fragments*—are mostly radioactive versions of otherwise normal atoms in the middle of the periodic table. They are radioactive by virtue of having too many or too few neutrons to be stable. The mechanism of decay usually involves spitting out electrons from the nucleus (because a neutron decays into a proton and an electron), often accompanied by a gamma (γ) ray, which is just like an x-ray, but for the mechanism that produces it.

That is, the waste from a nuclear reactor—the sum of all fission fragments—is radioactive. In fact, it is *violently* radioactive. Stay away from it.

But let us not be too simple-minded about the waste. We need to know the quantity, how long it lasts, and what we can do to protect ourselves.

Shielding

As to that last question, the waste from nuclear reactors is stored on the site of the power plant, because there is no long-term repository as yet. Everybody who works at the power plant works within a few hundred meters of all the waste the reactor has generated during its decades of operation. They are also within a few hundred meters of the reactor itself, which produces far more radiation than the waste does. Shielding is provided by ordinary materials like stainless steel and concrete. No ill health has arisen among the employees because of that radiation. Clearly, sensible measures are required to protect against that radiation, but nothing extreme is required.

Quantity

The quantity of radioactive waste is an issue that needs some discussion. Let us begin by thinking of a vial containing 1 cubic centimeter of some hypothetical poison. Now we take that poison and pour it into a liter of water. We have a liter of poisonous water, which is 1,000 times as "much" as we had when the poison was in the vial. If we pour the poison into a swimming pool, we now have perhaps 100,000 liters of contaminated water, 100 million times the volume we started with.

It is a fairly simple matter to calculate the quantity of radioactive waste that will result from operating a nuclear reactor for a certain length of time, because we know how many nuclei must undergo fission to product that much energy. To make the story short, if we have a nuclear reactor that produces 3 GW of heat power, resulting in 1 GW of electrical power, and we run it full tilt for one year, the resulting mass of fission fragments is one metric ton, 1,000 kg, the mass of one cubic meter of water.

In other words, operating a standard nuke for a year produces radioactive waste that weighs as much as a compact car.

As to the quantity of radioactive "contamination," the answer depends upon how the fission products are treated. Indeed, we often hear people telling us how much nuclear waste is hanging around to be disposed of. The mass of the fission fragments is 1,000 kg for every year of operation of a 1000-MWe power plant. If the fission products are left as they are, imbedded in what is mostly U-238 (actually an oxide of it), then the mass of the waste is (say) 30,000 kg. If we repackage the fuel rods in stainless steel canisters, the total weight might be 100,000 kg. If the spent fuel rods were converted to a powder and spread on the ground (no, this is not a recommendation), then the weight of the contaminated soil would be very large. (Fill in your own number.) On the other hand, if we "reprocess," meaning that we remove the waste from the fuel, then we are dealing with 1,000 kg, which can be dispersed into borosilicate glass and held in stainless steel jackets. Bear in mind that the hazard comes not from the bulk, but from the radioactive fission products.

Duration

As to how long the waste lasts, the answer is not simple. Some of the waste lasts less than a microsecond. Some of it lasts for millions of years. We measure *half-lives* of radioactive isotopes. That is the time that elapses before the radiation is reduced by half, owing to the fact that when the nucleus decays, it no longer exists. Each half-life cuts the radiation in half again. Ten half-lives result in 0.1% (actually, one part in 1024) of the original activity.

Eventually, all of an isotope will be gone. So imagine that we have a billion nuclei of a radioactive isotope. Eventually, all billion will be gone. About 99.9% of the isotopes will be gone (transmuted to something else) in 10 half-lives. If the half-life is one second, then all one billion of the radioactive events will occur in about 10 seconds. If the half-life is 100 years, then those billion events will be spread out over 1,000 years.

In other words, short half-lives are associated with high radioactivity. Long half-lives are associated with low radioactivity.

The oxygen in your body has an extremely long half-life—infinity, as far as we can tell—and presents no radiation hazard whatsoever.

There are some isotopes with very long half-lives in nuclear waste, but they do not come from fission. Some neutrons are absorbed by U-238, which becomes U-239. Two quick transitions later, the nucleus has become plutonium-239 (Pu-239), an isotope that behaves almost the same as U-235, as in Fig. 44. After years of presence in a nuclear reactor, there is a buildup of some Pu-239, Pu-240, americium (Am-241 that is used in smoke detectors), and a handful of other *transuranics*. One thing that limits the buildup of Pu-239 is the fact that it undergoes fission, just as U-235 does. Actually, about 40% of the energy from a nuclear reactor comes from Pu-239 that was created from U-238, not part of the fuel put into the reactor.

Accidents

It is physically impossible for a nuclear reactor to explode like a bomb. The only hazard from the nuclear cycle comes from exposure to radiation from radioactive materials. Figure 47 shows that US radiation exposure from nuclear power plants is utterly trivial. We get over 20 times as much radiation from consumer electronics as we get from industrial sources.

There have been two reactor accidents of note. The Three Mile Island accident harmed nobody, and only released some radioactive inert gases that were quickly dispersed and almost as quickly decayed to insignificance.

The Chernobyl accident was about as bad as an accident can get. There was no containment building, the reactor design was one that had been rejected decades before in the US, some technicians were playing around, and the graphite core became an inferno, putting about half of the radioactive fission products from the reactor into the atmosphere. There were about 30 deaths of firemen from intense radiation. There is considerable debate about the residual effects on people who were exposed to small amounts of radiation. In truth, there will be no definitive answer until actuarial data are obtained several decades into the future. But as of now, there are fewer than 50 deaths than can be attributed to that worst nuclear accident in history, and about the worst accident that *can* happen.

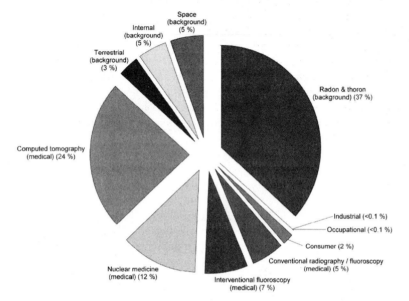

All Exposure Categories
Collective Effective Dose (percent), 2006

Figure 47: Radiation doses from various sources. (Thanks to Dan Strom of Battelle Northwest).

Virtually all of our exposure comes from natural and medical sources. Industrial (including nuclear power stations) and occupational exposures are both less than 0.1 percent of our exposure. The internal background comes mainly from potassium-40, a naturally occurring radioactive element. Consumer electronics, primarily cathode-ray tubes in television sets and computer screens are responsible for about 2% of our radiation dose.

Chapter 14   Biomass

After the OPEC oil embargoes, there was a spate of Split Wood Not Atoms bumper stickers, at least in New England where trees are plentiful. We understand that the bumper stickers didn't sell well in Western Kansas, where early farmers used stone fence posts because there were no trees for miles around.

There is a certain appeal to the notion of energy independence gained by burning wood from local trees rather than oil from medieval sheikdoms. However, the idea is more of a delusion than a dream, for at least three reasons: (1) tree growth could not possibly hope to keep up with demand for firewood; (2) pollution from wood burning is far greater than from burning petroleum; and (3) environmentalists oppose the concept.

Efficiency of Biomass Production

The term *biomass* refers to any matter that recently came into existence as a result of photosynthesis—trees, leaves, grass, corn, sugar cane, and weeds. The category includes secondary products such as ethanol derived from corn, and dung from domestic or wild animals. It also includes biodiesel.

We are usually concerned with the *amount* of such matter (produced, say, on a given plot of land during one growing season) usually reckoned in kilograms of *dry matter*. When the water content is removed, the *heat content* of all biomass is about the same, about 15 MJ/kg, which is about 1/2 that of the highest-grade coal and about 1/3 that of petroleum (see Table A3).

Every child learns in grade school—either by reading or by actually experimenting—that sunlight causes plant growth directly. If a portion of a leaf is covered with a dark sheet of paper, the leaf turns yellow in the covered area. In the wild, when one leaf totally blocks sunlight to another, the hidden leaf will wither and die. Ideally, a plant should have just enough leaf area to absorb all of the sunlight, but not so much that it puts out leaves that don't get enough sunlight to survive. The plant must meet those conditions in full sunlight, windy conditions, cloudy weather, at all times of the day, and at all times of the year when the weather is good enough to support plant life.

As it happens, most plants have about five times as much surface area as the land beneath them.[45] That is, the leaf area of the plants covering a hectare (10,000 m^2) of ground will have a total surface area of five hectares. But plants don't actually absorb all the sunlight even when growing conditions are ideal. Leaves are, after all, *green*. This means that they reflect green light, approximately the strongest portion of the solar spectrum. Chlorophyll absorbs light only in the blue and red portions of the spectrum, and not completely even there.[46] With no further information, we could confidently estimate that no more than about 20% of the energy in sunlight could become stored as biomass energy.

But we do know more. Generally, it requires the absorption of about ten photons of light in the red/infrared range to produce one carbohydrate molecule. "Of the 73×10^8 kcal [30×10^{12} joules] falling on an acre [4047 square meters] per year [3.16×10^7 seconds] in temperate latitudes, only about 0.1 to 0.5 percent is fixed as organic material," says L. F. Small.[47] Small's figures for insolation amount to 239 W/m^2, about equal to the average solar intensity in Albuquerque. The rates of fixing organic material, 0.1% and 0.5%, correspond to 0.239 W/m^2, and 1.19 W/m^2, respectively.

The most prolific growth of biomass I have been able to find is that of sugar cane grown in a subtropical environment.[48] Alan Lloyd, a professional engineer who has long lived in Hawaii described to me how the sugar cane is harvested. "Ordinary harvesting equipment won't work. They use a big D-8 [800-horsepower] Caterpillar tractor to smash down the sugar cane. Then they use big power shovels to hoist it onto trucks that haul it away to the sugar factory."

The production of biomass energy in this case amounts to 3.7 W/m^2.

Split Wood, Not Atoms!

Some New Englanders have a long tradition of cutting trees for firewood, *sustainably*, in the current jargon. In order not to deplete the forest, it is

---

[45] R. G. Loomis, W. A. Williams, and W. G. Duncan, "Community architecture and the productivity of terrestrial plant communities," in *Harvesting the Sun: Photosynthesis in Plant Life*, San Pietro, Greece, and Army, eds. (Academic Press, New York, 1967).

[46] C. T. deWitt, "Photosynthesis: Its Relationship to Overpopulation," in *Harvesting the Sun: Photosynthesis in Plant Life*, San Pietro, Greece, and Army, eds. (Academic Press, New York, 1967).

[47] Lawrence F. Small, Professor of Oceanography at Oregon State University, in Douglas Considine's *Energy Technology Handbook* (McGraw-Hill, 1977).

[48] Alfred L. Johnson, "Biomass Energy," Astronautics and Aeronautics 13:11, p. 64 (1975).

necessary to do selective cutting. Every year, an acre (about 0.4 hectares) of land can be farmed for about a half cord of firewood. (A cord is a pile of four-foot [1.2 meter] logs stacked four feet high in an eight-foot long stack, comprising 128 cubic feet [3.6 cubic meters] of wood and air.)

Let's not lose track of the goal, which is to express all solar notions in SI units for easy comparison. The half-cord represents a certain amount of thermal energy—16 billion joules; the land area is one acre (4047 square meters); and the time is one year (31.6 million seconds). Dividing the energy by the time, we find that our acre of forest produced a mere 500 watts of power (average energy stored per unit time). Dividing the 500 watts by the 4047 square meters yields about 0.12 W/m^2, representing an efficiency of about 0.06% for converting sunlight into chemical energy stored in the wood.

Imagine, now, that the entire United States is covered with trees that produce firewood as abundantly as New England forests. The sustainable yield of firewood would amount to about 970 GW_t (thermal), a mere 30 percent of our 2008 around-the-clock consumption rate of 3,560 GW_t (3.56 TW_t). Of course, at least half of the US is utterly incapable of producing trees at the prodigious rate of New England forests. Helping to make our case for us are Paul and Anne Ehrlich, who say,

> "Humanity now obtains about 1.5 TW [terawatt, 10^{12} watts, thermal] by using biomass fuels—fuelwood, crop wastes, and dung." [referring to heat, not electricity] ... Burning residues or dung is a desperation measure taken by destitute people lacking other fuel sources. Using these materials as fuel leads to a steady depletion of soil nutrients and fertility, causing a stark deterioration of farmland... "

> Paul & Anne Ehrlich (1991)

The *Annual Energy Review 2008* says that the total non-hydro energy (geothermal, wood, waste, solar and wind) produced worldwide in 2006 was 7.47 quads (7.88 EJ), equivalent to 0.249 TWt, which is considerably less than the Ehrlichs reported in 1991. Very likely, the EIA did not include household use of marginal fuels for cooking and heating. These figures should be compared with US average power consumption of 3.5 TWe (all sources) and a worldwide average of 15.7 TWe.

The speaker for the April 1, 2002, meeting of the Colorado Section of the American Chemical Society is Dr. Henry R. Bungay of Rensselaer Polytechnic Institute. His talk is entitled, "Confessions of a Bioenergy Advocate." Read on.

> "Abstract: Two decades after publication of his prize-winning book, "Energy, The Biomass Options", bioenergy is still

inching toward significance. Its proponents have found major support in the U.S. Senate by touting reduction in petroleum imports, slower global warming, and converting wastes to energy. This presentation surveys the technology, assesses feedstocks, estimates the potential amount of biomass energy, and predicts economics. *The bottom line is that bioenergy is commercially viable but its **maximum potential contribution is about equal to the current annual increase** in the world's need for power.*" [Emphasis added]

Ethanol From Corn!

One of those manifestations of solar energy is ethyl alcohol (*a.k.a.* ethanol, *a.k.a.* EtOH) from corn, known as "liquid sunshine" to solar enthusiasts. Ethanol is the same alcohol (CH_3CH_2OH) that is in beer, wine, and distilled spirits. The process of producing EtOH from corn begins with using the very same yeast that consume sugar and produce EtOH as a byproduct.

As they produce more and more EtOH, the yeasts are living in their own offal, so to speak. After the concentration of EtOH becomes higher than about 10% (depending upon the strain of yeast), the yeasts can no longer function; in fact, they die.

On the early American frontier, the "proof" of good liquor was that it was flammable. As it happens, a mixture of water and EtOH will not burn until the concentration of EtOH is 50%, well beyond the capabilities of yeast. For this reason 100-proof became associated with 50% concentration. (Pure EtOH is 200-proof.)

The 90%/10% mixture of water and EtOH produced by yeast will not burn; it is not a fuel. Therefore, something needs to be done to the "mash" left after the yeast have had their day. That something is distillation—boiling the mixture and then re-condensing the EtOH-rich vapor—repeatedly until the concentration of EtOH is high enough. (It is impossible to get beyond 190-proof without adding benzene, which must then be removed if the EtOH is to be drunk.) The amount of energy that must be used for distillation is obviously large. How large? Read on.

The Ethanol Lobby

In gasoline, EtOH increases the octane rating. The Environmental Protection Agency in the Clinton years ruled that gasoline manufacturers were required to add EtOH into gasoline as an oxygenate; moreover, the EtOH was *required* to be derived from corn. The oil companies sued the EPA in federal court. The court ruled that the EPA had the right (on grounds of protecting air quality) to establish the EtOH content of gasoline, but did *not* have the right to specify the source. In truth, EtOH is obtained more cheaply from petroleum than from biological sources like corn. Later, Congress got around that Supreme Court decision by writing a law that demanded that gasoline be supplemented by EtOH *from corn.*

The reason for adding oxygenates—EtOH, or in some places, MBTE (methyl tertiary-butyl ether)—to gasoline is ostensibly to get a cleaner burn. I quote from a letter to Chemical and Engineering News[49] about EtOH: "Perhaps readers should be reminded that this oxygenate is not needed in cars manufactured after 1995." [emphasis added.]

The Wall Street Journal[50] pretends no expertise in science, of course, but they understand money. "The economics haven't done anything to change the ethanol industry's strong appetite for government subsidies. ... Between 1998 and 2001, the GAO estimated, the subsidy removed $3.86 billion from the Highway Trust Fund".[50]

Archer Daniels Midland, the major corporate entity behind EtOH, is obviously part of the ethanol lobby, as their main concern is farming and farm products. But there are also manufacturers of equipment for distillation and transportation of the EtOH product.

How much subsidy does ADM get? According to James Bovard,[51] "Every $1 of profits earned by ADM's corn sweetener operation costs consumers $10, and every $1 of profits earned by its ethanol operation costs taxpayers $30."

In 1997, I had some communications with a manufacturer[52] of distillation equipment for the production of ethanol from corn. He was unwilling to divulge how much energy actually was used in the production of EtOH from corn. In fact, he was very evasive and defensive and refused to provide any data at all. He was obviously trying to hide and/or make excuses for very low (or even negative) energy production. There was no point in trying to nail that custard pie to the wall.

C. John Mann, Professor Emeritus of Geology at the Urbana-Champagne campus of the University of Illinois, writes[53], "Make no mistake, ethanol comes at a high price. Ethanol producers receive a 53-cents-a-gallon tax credit for ethanol."

---

[49] John P. Collman, "Environmental articles lack perspective," Letter to *C&E News* (June 17, 2002).

[50] John J. Fialka, "Years of Subsidies Now Put Ethanol on Verge of Victory," *Wall Street Journal* (Aug 23, 2002). Thanks to Arthur B. Harris.

[51] http://www.cato.org/pubs/pas/pa-241.html James Bovard, "Archer Daniels Midland: *A Case Study In Corporate Welfare* (Policy Analysis #241, Cato Institute, September 26, 1995).

[52] Name omitted to protect the guilty.

[53] C. John Mann, "Promise of ethanol comes with high price," *The News Gazette* (May 12, 2002). Thanks to Tom Phipps for this article.

In the Still of the Night

Fortunately, data can be obtained from people who are interested in facts rather than in preserving their financial interests.

According to Cornell Professor David Pimentel[54], there is a net energy *loss* of about 18.9 MJ for every kilogram (given by him as 54,000 BTU for every gallon) of EtOH. *That is, it takes more energy to produce EtOH than you can get out of the EtOH.*

More recently Pimentel[55] chaired a US Department of Energy panel to investigate the energetics of ethanol production. They found that "131,000 BTUs are needed to make 1 gallon of ethanol. One gallon of ethanol has an energy value of only 77,000 BTU. ... there is a net energy loss of 54,000 BTU [per gallon]."

He continues, "That helps explain why fossil fuels—not ethanol—are used to produce ethanol."

But there are other costs as well. Erosion of soils occurs 12 times as fast with corn growing as with other crops, and corn requires 25% more water.

Ignoring the minor matter of negative efficiency, Pimentel goes on to say, "If all the automobiles in the United States were fueled with 100 percent ethanol, a total of 97% of the U.S. land area would be needed to grow the corn feedstock."

Pimentel's data are somewhat naïve, according to some experts, primarily because he did not include the energy value inherent in the dried mash. Those who wish to see details should consult the thorough Shapouri paper[56] on the net.

Shapouri *et al.* use the following data: The heat value of EtOH = 76,000 BTU/gallon; corn is produced on good farms at 122 bushels per acre per year; and one bushel of corn yields 2.55 gallons of EtOH. They use data from the literature to account for all possible inputs, losses, and residuals to arrive at the following statement: "...for every BTU dedicated to producing ethanol, there is a 24-percent energy gain."

A DOE report[57] says that 27,750 BTU (29.3 MJ) per gallon (3.8liters) are required to distill EtOH to 190 proof. Using Shapouri's figure for the heat value of EtOH, we see that 36.5 percent of the energy in EtOH is used in the distillation process alone.

---

[54] David Pimentel, "Energy and Dollar Costs of Ethanol Production with Corn," Hubbert Center Newsletter #98/2 (Apr. 1998).

[55] http://unisci.com/stories/20013/0813012.htm

[56] Hosein Shapouri, James A. Duffield, and Michael S. Graboski, "Estimating the Net Energy Balance of Corn Ethanol" (paper AER-721): www.ethanolrfa.org. (rfa = Renewable Fuels Assoc.)

[57] General USDOE-SSFAPP Plant Description,http://www.beienginc.com/id13.html

I do not intend to challenge these figures; in fact, the background research seems to have been very carefully done. I do, however, intend to put their numbers into perspective by converting to SI units for solar intensity—watts per square meter.

Readers not interested in the arithmetic may skip forward to the results in the next paragraph. We want to find the productivity in units of average watts per square meter of land area so that we can compare the answer directly with average sunlight, which is measured in the same units. We begin by multiplying 76,000 BTU per gallon by 2.55 gallons per bushel, and then by 122 bushels per acre per year to yield 23.6 million BTU of EtOH energy per acre per year. We multiply that result by 1055 J/BTU to convert the energy to joules, and divide by the 31.6 million seconds in a year obtain a year-round average gross power of 789 watts per acre, or 0.195 watts per square meter. By comparison, year-round average sunlight is 1000 times as large, namely 200 watts per square meter. If these results are not low enough to be discouraging, let us remember that these values are only 24% greater than the average power input to produce the EtOH. That is, 600 watts per acre is the annual average power required from fossil fuels to produce 789 watts per acre.

When we simply ignore the energy used to produce the EtOH, we are still left with the fact that the around-the-clock average power available from EtOH production from corn amounts to a paltry 189 watts per acre, or 0.047 watts per square meter. If corn-derived EtOH were used to produce electricity at an efficiency of 33%, one acre's worth of corn could keep a 60-watt light bulb burning continuously. We remind the reader that Shapouri *et al.* use the most optimistic figures: the *best* corn yield; the *least* energy used to produce fertilizer; the *least* energy required for farming; the *most efficient* distillation techniques; the *most* residual energy (in the form of mash); and generally *the most favorable* (but still credible) values for any and all aspects of EtOH production.

Suppose that we could establish huge farms for EtOH production to supply the entire US with energy. Ethanol production yields a net 0.047 W/m^2, some 4300 times smaller than the 200 W/m^2 average US insolation (intensity). All we would need would be nearly seven times the land area of US, devoted to EtOH production, using the most efficient methods on the planet, with no land set aside for cities or National Parks, to produce the energy used in the US.

Manure!

Chicken farms, dairy farms, and feed lots produce prodigious quantities of manure. It is possible to process the manure to produce methane, the principal component of natural gas. Getting rid of manure and producing energy while doing so are both laudable goals.

Typical of articles found in the popular press is one in *The Hartford Courant*[58], in which the electrical power output from the methane works out to about 100 watts per head of cattle. Another is from the Environmental Protection Agency (see Ref. 25), according to which

> "Dairy cows provide the major recoverable animal manure resource in Washington. In 1992 the manure generated by about 242,000 dairy cows had the potential to produce 26 aMW of electric power. The generating potential is based on the rule of thumb of slightly more than 0.1 aMW per thousand head of dairy cows."

And what's *aMW*? It's *alternative* megawatts. Note again that 26 million watts divided by 242,000 cows is 107 watts per cow. Similarly, a farmer in Durham, California[59] is producing 40 kW from the manure produced by 320 cows, amounting to 125 W/cow.

In fertile places where one acre of well-fertilized land can support one head of cattle (two head per hectare) exclusive of the grain fed at milking time), these figures amount to about 100–125 watts per acre, or about 0.025–0.03 W/m^2. Sunlight stores energy in vegetable matter, cows use some of that energy, the methane digester uses some of the energy that is left in the manure, and the methane contains the residual. Heat lost in the production of electricity consumes even more. The overall efficiency of converting sunlight to electricity is low, as one would expect, around 0.015% at best.

Expectations

Of course, biomass does have its place in energy production. We in the US obtain a little over 3 percent of our energy from biomass.

One way to increase the production of biomass energy would be to convert farmland from the production of wheat to the production of some hypothetical energy crop. That's a pretty unlikely scenario, given that people like to eat.

Another would be to use more fertilizers.

Another way would be to irrigate the deserts of the world with desalinated seawater. But the energy requirements for desalination could not be met by solar systems, least of all by the power generated from the biomass grown from the newly irrigated land. Nor could solar systems

---

[58] The Hartford Courant [5/13/97]
[59] http://www.jgpress.com/BCArticles/2001/030146.html

provide the power required to pump water up[60] to high elevations like Utah, Nevada, New Mexico, and much of the Great Plains.

We note for the record that environmentalists have expressed their opposition to all of these methods.

That is, there is very little likelihood that biomass energy production can increase appreciably beyond its present production, and everybody would obviously oppose devoting the entire US land area to production of energy crops.

---

[60] In hydropower plants, water descends and produces electrical power. To use electrical power to pump water to a higher elevation should be called *inverse* hydropower.

Chapter 15   Photovoltaics

Of course, when the topic of solar electricity comes up, people naturally think of direct electronic conversion of sunlight to electricity without involving any heat, using solar cells. The devices for converting light to electricity are called *photovoltaic* (PV) cells.

It all seems to be magic. Sunlight in. Electricity out. But there's a limit to the magic. Solar cells cannot create energy. They can only convert some of the solar energy—and certainly not all of it—to electricity. Nor can the solar cell in New York convert the sunlight hitting Bangladesh into electricity. The solar cell can convert only the sunlight that the solar cell absorbs.

Most solar cells are small. Correspondingly, they can only produce small amounts of electricity. Knowing absolutely nothing about solar-cell manufacture, nothing about their characteristics, and nothing about their cost, we can establish an upper limit to their performance. The 1-cm by 4-cm solar cell on a calculator could produce a whopping 0.08 watts in full sunlight *if* its efficiency were (impossibly) 100%; in reality, its efficiency is between 5% and 10%, so it produces between 0.004 and 0.008 watts in full sunlight. In a brightly lit room the cell will produce 100 times less power. Fortunately the calculator is able to run on flea power.

Limitations on the efficiency of photocells

People like to refer to "a quantum leap" as if it were something big. That isn't even close to the meaning of the term. Let me explain.

In an atom, electrons are confined to various states. We might visualize those states as small branches on a tree, and the electrons as birds. One branch might hold two birds and another might hold eight. Whenever a branch is full, no more birds are allowed. We will assume that the lower branches are more desirable. We will also assume that there is an overall limit on the number of birds on the tree, even though many upper branches are unoccupied. (Remember, we're not really talking about the laws of bird behavior, but making an analogy for atoms.)

Suppose that a bird from a lower branch flies away. A bird from one of the upper branches may fly down to occupy the vacancy. The bird has made a *quantum leap* of, say, two meters downward. Alternatively, given incentive, a bird might fly upward to an unoccupied branch one meter above. That, too, is a quantum leap. The important idea is that the amount of leap is a fixed quantity (two meters, one meter, …). The bird cannot occupy a branch that is 1.7525 meters down from its perch, simply because there is no branch there.

At the atomic scale, there are *energy states* that electrons may occupy, but electrons may not occupy non-states. An electron may *transit* from one state to another. In doing so, it must either absorb or release energy of the exact amount to account for the difference in energy between the two states. The quantum leap refers to *energy*, not to location.

The amounts of energy we are talking about are tiny. Because we are dealing with tiny electrical charge of single electrons, and because we measure electrical potential in volts, physicists find it convenient to use a tiny unit of energy called the electron-volt, or eV, the amount of kinetic energy gained by an electron in moving across a potential of one volt. One eV is 0.000 000 000 000 000 000 16 joules, expressed as 0.16 attojoules (aJ).

If an electron moves from one energy state of 5 eV to another of 6 eV, it requires 1 eV of energy to do so. If it goes from the 6-eV state to the 5-eV state, it will release 1 eV, possibly as heat, possibly as light in the infrared region. The *quantum* aspect refers to the well-defined states and the well-defined energy differences. To repeat, a *quantum leap* has nothing to do with the adjective *big*.

Light, including sunlight, seems to consist of little bundles of energy called *quanta* (Einstein's terminology) or *photons* (modern terminology). Each photon has a certain amount of energy. The shorter the wavelength, the higher the energy. On the blue end of the spectrum, photons have about 3 eV, and on the red end, about 1.8 eV.

The Quantum Limitation

Photocells consist of a pair of dissimilar semiconductors joined together. The details are of no great concern to us; the only thing that matters is that photons of light striking the surface cause electrons to undergo a quantum leap. The energy gap of that leap is called the *band-gap*. That leap is the source of the electrical current that the PV cell produces.

In silicon solar cells, the band-gap is 1.1 eV. This energy corresponds to a wavelength of about 1130 nm, which lies in the infrared portion of the spectrum. Refer to Fig. 48. Photons of less than 1.1 eV energy (wavelengths longer that 1130 nm) cannot cause the transition to occur. (Think of the birds simply not having the energy to fly to the upper branch.)

If, on the other hand, a photon of 2.5 eV (about 500 nm in Fig. 48) strikes the PV cell, it has plenty of energy to cause the quantum transition. In fact, it has 1.4 eV more than necessary. The problem is that the excess energy is simply wasted as heat.

In Fig. 48, we show the solar spectrum (leaving out many bumps and wiggles) as the heavy curve. The 1.1 eV energy is marked on the wavelength scale as the border between having too little energy and too much energy.

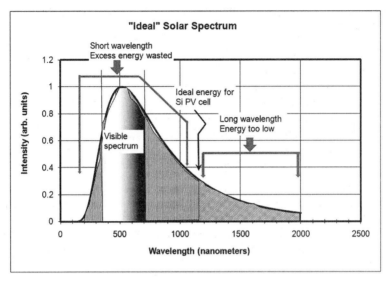

Figure 48: The "ideal" solar spectrum (no account taken of atmospheric absorption) as it applies to silicon PV cells.

Now we come to the main limitation of PV cells. We ask a broad spectrum—sunlight, ranging from infrared to ultraviolet—to do a quantum job, causing electrons to transit between well-defined states. No matter whether the transition involves 1.1 eV or 2.8 eV or any other number of your choosing, some light will always be useless because its energy is too low. Other light will always have too much energy, and the excess will be wasted as heat. For that reason, PV cells are inherently limited as to their efficiency. As a matter of practical concern, the best solar cells available on a large scale have an efficiency of about 12%.

Best Uses of PV Cells

The output power of a PV cell varies with the amount of sunlight. Under what kinds of loads would the output of PV cells always be maximized for every intensity of sunlight? In Appendix B we show that the output voltage must remain approximately constant, somewhat below the maximum attainable, for all intensity levels. What sorts of electrically powered things might be consistent with this property?

Neither incandescent lights nor electric motors fall into that category. Both fluorescent lights and light-emitting diodes do, but it's generally pointless to convert light to light simultaneously while throwing away most of the energy.

So, if PV cells are unsuitable for producing light or motion, how can they be used? There are some applications for which PV cells are suitable (and one is *very* questionable)

- Electrolysis of water to produce hydrogen. The theoretical voltage for electrolyzing water is 1.24 volts. If the electrical resistance of water were exactly zero, all electrolysis cells would operate at exactly 1.24 volts, regardless of the current flow. To get more current, hence a higher rate of hydrogen production, requires one to raise the voltage, because the electrical resistance is most assuredly not zero.

I have data on a commercial unit that hydrolyzes water with an efficiency of about 62%. Assuming that one could get the same efficiency with PV cells of 12% efficiency, and the hydrogen were used in fuel cells of 60% efficiency, the overall efficiency from sunlight to fuel cell would be about 3.7% (if we ignore the problems of collection and transportation of the hydrogen.

- Charging batteries. Batteries are best charged by a constant voltage, and the charging current merely determines how fast the job is done.

Indeed, this is the most frequent application, with good reason. Off-the-grid homeowners use their PV cells to charge batteries that are, in turn, used to run lights and appliances. It is often necessary to provide lighted signs on highways under construction where access to the grid is impractical. PV cells keep batteries charged, and the batteries provide power for the lights. The overall efficiency of delivering power to the load is the efficiency of the PV cell multiplied by the efficiency of the battery charger multiplied by the efficiency of the battery itself (wherein we must account for any energy losses by internal battery currents).

- Finally, the PV cells can provide power to anything at all, providing that there is an immediate back-up system to compensate for the variations in the PV's output power, allowing the PV array to operate at constant voltage.

Possible, but expensive!

Exotic materials!

There is a seductive fallacy about solar cells. We hear, "Silicon is one of the most abundant elements in the earth's crust. Solar cells are made from silicon. Therefore, silicon PV cells are made from readily available materials."

Silicon (Si) is extremely abundant, 30% of the mass of every grain of sand in the world. That sand is not a PV cell, nor is the silicon that is extracted from the sand. But the availability of sand is not the limiting factor. To make a PV cell means to "dope" the silicon with other elements to cause the device to have semiconductor properties. When all is said and done, the Si-based PV modules usually have an efficiency of 12% or less. The efficiency is low because the band-gap of silicon—1.1 eV—is so low that most of the spectral energy is wasted as heat.

To make PV cells of higher efficiency requires exotic materials, including germanium, gallium, antimony, indium, and cadmium, possibly with gold or platinum for conductors. Efficiencies of up to about 40% have been achieved in fingernail-sized PV multi-bandgap cells made with exotic materials.

There is a trade-off between efficiency and area. Given the desire to generate (say) 10 MW from photovoltaics, the use of cells with 20 percent efficiency would require only half the surface area that would be required with cells of 10 percent efficiency. But if the more efficient cells cost (say) 5 times as much to purchase and install, it would be cheaper to use the less efficient cells.

A study by the American Physical Society (APS)[61] asked how much material would be required to produce 1% of the US electricity by the turn of the century. They found, for example, that 250 metric tons of germanium would be required, which is over three times the world's annual production. It would require nearly twenty times the world's annual production of gallium. Some 17 percent of the US annual production of cement would be devoted to making the *structure* to hold the flat-plate solar collectors. Nothing important has changed since the 1979 APS report, save that we now (2008) use 87% more electricity.

The Price Will Fall Through the Floor!

Another seductive fallacy is that mass production will cause the price of PV cells to drop the same way that the price of computing power has dropped. Solar enthusiasts incessantly tell us that the price of PV will drop through the floor, because the price of computer components has done so. Just look at how the price of computing has plummeted during the last several decades!

Computers have gotten faster because manufacturers are able to put more and more transistors into smaller and smaller areas, tens of millions of them in the area covered by your fingernail. The smaller the transistors, the

---

[61] Solar Photovoltaic Energy Conversion: Principal Conclusions of the American Physical Society Study Group on, H. Ehrenreich, Chairman, (American Physical Society, January, 1979).

smaller the distance that signals have to travel, and the smaller amounts of energy that have to be stored and released. The speed of computation is inherently linked to the small size and high-density packing of transistors in integrated circuits. The price *per transistor* continues to plummet, as it has done for decades. The price *per square millimeter* of integrated circuit decreased rapidly at first, but has bottomed out.

By contrast, the name of the game in PV is *Real Estate*. To intercept huge amounts of sunlight, you have to cover huge areas with PV cells, and the size of the individual cells is of no relevance at all. The price per square centimeter of solar cells decreased rapidly at first, but has now stabilized.

Figure 49 shows the average cost of photovoltaic cells and modules from 1989 to 2007 in dollars per peak watt. The general trend is downward as expected when the expanding market causes increases in production efficiency. However, the decrease is totally out of scale with the decrease in transistor costs in computer processing chips.

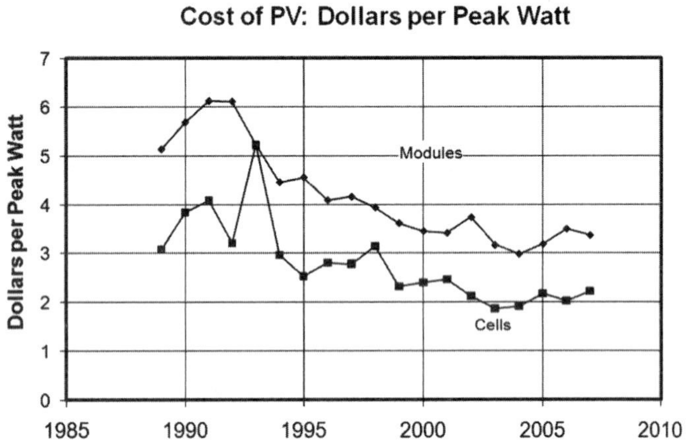

Cost of PV: Dollars per Peak Watt

Figure 49: US average cost per watt of PV cells and modules, 1989-2007.

The EIA offers no explanation for the anomalously high cell price in 1993.

Figure 50 shows the rapid decline in price per transistor in computer central processing units[62] from 1968 to 2002. Using 1989 as a reference for 100,

---

[62] http://www.kurzweilai.net/articles/art0593.html?printable=1 (integrated circuit data from Intel; PV price data from *Annual Energy Review*

the price has dropped from about 3 million down to 0.75 from 1968 to 2002 (notice the logarithmic scale, in which each mark on the vertical axis corresponds to a factor of 10). The Energy Information Agency began keeping track of prices for photovoltaics in 1989. From then until 2001, the price per peak kilowatt of PV had dropped only about 20% to 30%.

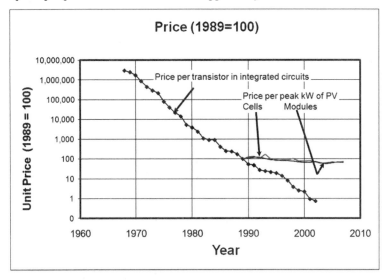

Figure 50: Relative price (1989 = 100) per transistor in integrated circuits and per peak kW of PV cells (logarithmic scale) from 1968 to 2007.

In the 1989-2002 interval while PV prices dropped by 20% to 30%, the price of transistors in CPUs has dropped by over 99%. Since 2002, the PV price has remained static.

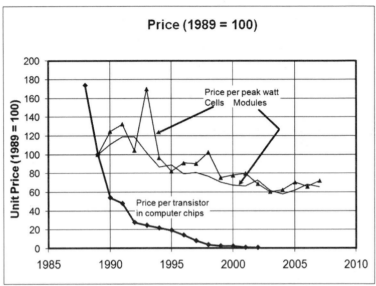

Figure 51: Relative price (1989 = 100) per transistor in integrated circuits and per peak kW of PV cells (linear scale), 1989-2007.

It would require on the order of 22,000 square kilometers—about 33% bigger than the land area of Connecticut (but located in sunnier climes)—of PV cells at 12% efficiency—packed edge-to-edge, with no room for squirrels, let alone room for roads and houses—to collect enough sunlight to power the nation's electrical grid. At this date, the *total* amount of PV sold in the US from 1989 to 2007 amounts to 1.8 GWe (peak), or less than 300 MW around-the-year average power. Assuming 12% efficiency for the collectors and 950 W/m^2 solar intensity, we can calculate that the total area of the collectors sold in the US through 2007 is about 15 square kilometers.

Many nuclear power plants usually produce about 1.3 GW, and do so around the clock. Thus, one such plant produces about four times as much energy every year as all of the photovoltaics ever sold in the country.

Presently, wind turbines (exclusive of any connection to the grid) cost about $1.00 per installed watt, and have an annual capacity factor of about 35%. The cost of PV modules (F.O.B. factory, neither fastened in place nor connected to the grid) is presently about $3.37 per peak watt, and the capacity factor is only about 15% to 20% *in the desert*. This makes PV at least seven times as expensive as wind for the same amount of energy produced, and no wind farm on the planet survives without massive subsidies.

The Long Island Lighting Authority (LIPA) has released a subsidy plan that can only be the result of severe arm-twisting. "So far, LIPA has provided some $3.6 million in rebates for residential solar installations," through a subsidy plan that gives customers $5.00 (2002, $6.00 previously) for every peak watt of rooftop PV cells they install.[63] The $3.6 million they have given away has resulted in an annual production of about 822,000 kilowatt-hours, worth about $100,000 (Long Island retail rates), or about $25,000 (Long Island wholesale rates) annually. It'll only take a few centuries for the PV cells to generate the subsidy the LIPA has paid. Of course, the money comes from the pockets of customers, not of LIPA.

Suppose that we wanted to generate enough power from PV cells to be equivalent to 1000 MWe of electricity around-the-clock—equal to one large conventional power plant—using PV cells of 12% efficiency and year-round average sunlight at 200 W/m². We would require 40 million square meters (16 square miles) of solar collector. This is about three times the total US production of PV cells in the nine-year period 1982–2007 (inclusive).

The American Physical Society study [Ref. 61] concluded:

> "Because of the costs associated with encapsulation, foundations, support structure, and installation of PV array fields, there is a large economic penalty for use of low efficiency cells. To compete in the U.S. central power generation market, *even zero-cost PV cells must have a limiting minimum efficiency.* The use of modules with efficiency as low as 10% will probably require substantial reduction in these other costs, even if the modules themselves are inexpensive." [emphasis added]

The APS concluded, in other words, that the cost of solar PV electricity would be prohibitively expensive even if the cells themselves were *free* ("zero-cost"), unless the efficiency were high.

The APS does not even mention the costs associated with storage, because they recognized that "it is unlikely that photovoltaics will contribute more than about 1% of the US electrical energy produced near the end of the [20th] century." [Ref. 61.] Indeed, the APS was correct. Good numbers and good physics led to good predictions.

As we have seen, the PV cells are only *part* of the high cost.

Use the Deserts!

The best place in the US for solar collectors of any sort is the desert Southwest. That is, of course, why both Solar-Two and the SEGS units are

---

[63] Uniondale, NY, USA: "LIPA Releases Draft Long Island Energy Plan" http://www.solarbuzz.com/News/NewsNAPR124.htm (October 23, 2002)

in the Mojave Desert. But for the industrial scale of solar collectors envisioned by solar enthusiasts, we cannot ignore the difficulties in transmitting power to other parts of the nation or the lack of water necessary for keeping the solar collectors clean. Nor can we ignore the power-line losses in transmitting electricity from the Mojave to distant eastern cities.

We read many arguments in favor of decentralization, saying that the costs (in materials, money, and energy) associated with transmitting power from big stations to customers are intolerably large. However, if there were large energy-producing facilities in the deserts, how would the energy be delivered to New York, Boston, Washington, D.C., Philadelphia, Atlanta, and Chicago, thousands of kilometers distant? High-voltage power lines? Through whose neighborhood? All of those problems would be exacerbated if the generating facilities were in the desert Southwest.

Put 'em on the Roof!

There are about 100 million homes in the United States, single-family houses and apartments included. For the sake of argument, let us assume that every one of them occupies 150 square meters of land area. That amounts to 15 billion square meters. Hypothetically, if *every* roof were fully covered with solar cells at 12% efficiency, every square meter could generate a year-round average of 24 watts per square meter. That amounts to 360 GW_e.

Life isn't that simple. Apartment dwellers have virtually no roof area available to themselves. Houses usually have a roofline that extends north-south or east-west. The houses best suited to solar collectors are those with a southern exposure.

But there are more problems. Most houses are in cities or suburbs. A characteristic of people in such places it to plant trees, often deliberately on the south side of the house to shade the house in summer. In the largely treeless west, you can spot towns miles away simply because they have trees.

All things considered, rooftops on American homes might be able to generate a year-round average of about 10 to 20 GW_e. Even that possibility is entirely hypothetical, of course. Most people cannot afford to cover even part, let alone the entire south-facing roof with solar collectors.

In fact, photovoltaic arrays are being put on rooftops mostly courtesy of taxpayers. For example, a new 127-kW (peak) photovoltaic array has been installed on the roof of a U.S. Postal Service processing plant 11 miles southwest of downtown Los Angeles. The array is the size of a football field. Winston Hickox, secretary of the state Environmental Protection

Agency cooed, "Relying on solar energy is no longer just a feel-good endeavor."[64]

And how good is this beauty? It will provide a whopping 10% of the facility's electricity during peak hours, when there is the least need for interior lighting. A ten-football-field area could provide 100% of the power during peak hours. Fifty or sixty football fields' worth of PV could provide enough energy around the clock—if they had a 100%-efficient storage and retrieval system.

With generous subsidies from both the federal government and the state government, the system cost the post office only $225,000. That amounts to $1.77 per installed peak watt and about $10 per installed average watt.

Happy Regrets

The Swiss government "regrets the early end of the solar photovoltaic subsidy program,"[65] that had "resulted in 378 installations across Switzerland". All together, the PV installations produce a whopping 3,660 megawatt-hours of electricity annually, about as much as a nuke produces during the playing of one football game.

The Swiss plan, of course, was to increase the contribution of renewable energy sources to the overall energy supply. "The overall goal of the wider program, which started in 1990 was to increase renewable energy usage by 0.5% over 10 years. In fact, an increase of 0.7% was achieved, with significant contributions coming from wood and biomass," says *Newsbuzz*[65] without saying *how much* of the contribution actually came from the highly vaunted photovoltaics.

Switzerland generates about 67 million megawatt-hours per year, so the annual 3,660 megawatt-hours is a piddling 0.0005 percent of the total. Said another way, if they subsidized 6.9 million PV installations instead of the mere 378, they could produce as much energy from PV as they do from their conventional power sources. That is, if they had a method to store the energy.

Solar Cars!

Every year engineering schools have a race to determine which school's students produce the best solar cars. The students learn a lot from the exercise, especially in how to reduce the weight and air resistance of

---

[64] Sandra Marquez, "Largest solar power grid on roof of postal processing plant," Associated Press Story, (April 13, 2002)

[65] Berne, Switzerland: "Swiss Report regrets early end of the PV subsidy program," http://www.solarbuzz.com/News/NewsEUGO24.htm October 22, 2002

vehicles, and how to make the most of the very little power they have at their disposal. It is a good engineering project that brings out the best engineering talents in the competitors. Every single student learns by direct experience that the world's transportation system will not be based on solar cars and trucks. They also learn that if the efficiency of the PV cells were 100%, the available power would still be too small for any practical vehicles. Invariably, the solar cars are small, cramped, uncomfortable, slow, extremely dangerous in case of accident, and devoid of amenities. They run only where and when the sunlight is intense; no Alaskan will use one in February to go out to get a bottle of milk.

Ideas for the future

Solar cells that are large enough to be useful for solar applications are about 12% efficient. Small experimental PV cells made of exotic materials have achieved much higher efficiencies, some in the range of 40%.[66] It is to be hoped that high efficiency can be obtained for solar cells that can be mass-produced so that large areas can be covered cheaply.

The primary method of attack is to make the PV cell in layers. The layer facing the sun uses blue light, but is transparent to all other colors. The next layer down absorbs green light and is transparent to all longer wavelengths, and so on. Everything is engineered so that if a given amount of sunlight causes a million transitions in the "blue" layer, it will also cause a million transitions in each other layer. The current must be the same in all layers, and will be limited by the current in the weakest layer.

That is not quite the whole story. At all times, there is a battle between electron promotion and recombination. The more intense the sunlight, the more promotion is going on, so there is an advantage to having solar concentrators (lenses, basically) that increase solar concentration over 100-fold. As a consequence, the orientation of the device becomes critically important, lest the tiny focusing spot miss the solar cell.

Be reminded that the most democratic institution on earth is the periodic table, found in classrooms throughout the world. This list contains the elements—*all* of them—that exist for constructing PV cells (or anything else). The new 40%-efficient device[66] is made of gallium (Ga), indium (In), phosphorus (P), arsenic (As), and germanium (Ge). The reward for developing reliable, inexpensive, high-efficiency PV cells will easily be in the billions of dollars, as everybody has recognized from the outset. Still, despite many decades of corporate and university research, such PV cells

---

[66] By Lisa Zyga "40% efficient solar cells to be used for solar electricity," June 1st, 2007, at http://www.physorg.com/news99904887.html

have not been developed. Although high efficiency has been attained, low price for such cells has not.

Chapter 16   Miscellaneous Non-Solar "Renewable" Sources

There are some renewable sources of energy that are not actually solar energy. Geothermal energy arises from the decay of radioactive elements deep within the earth, and has nothing to do with sunlight. There is a virtually infinite supply of geothermal energy, but it is very hard to use.

Oceanic waves are due to winds (indirectly due to solar energy), but tides are due to the relative motions of earth, moon, and sun, and not due to sunlight. The high tides at a few well-known tidal basins like the Bay of Fundy are due to the geometrical features of the water channel.

Although these sources are considerably different from those discussed in the rest of the book, we should discuss them, albeit briefly.

Geothermal Energy

The source of geothermal energy is radioactive materials found throughout the volume of the earth. The temperature of the interior is high because of that radiation and because the earth's crust provides an effective barrier against the transmission of heat.

Generally, the deeper you drill into the earth, the hotter it gets. However, there are places where hot magma is not very deep at all; Hawaiians can go watch lava ooze out of the ground. Icelanders get most of their energy—both heat and electricity—from geothermal sources.

There is enough energy in the bowels of the earth to last the human inhabitants forever. But how can we *use* that energy? Our techniques are primitive, but it is certain that our technology will improve.

When we extract energy from *anything*, the energy of that source diminishes, and geothermal hot-spots are no exception. The geothermal power plants in Middletown, California's misnamed "geysers region" produced 2000 MWe of electricity—the equivalent of two large conventional power plants—in the 1980s, but can now produce only 850 MWe.[67]

The diminution of power is not a reason not to develop geothermal power, of course. What it means in practical terms is that the hunt for more

---

[67] Jennifer Coleman, "Running out of steam: Geothermal field tapped out as alternative energy source," Associated Press (*Pueblo Chieftain*, Apr. 15, 2001).

geothermal energy is a never-ending project, not unlike the quest for petroleum.

Waves

Oceanic waves are also an indirect source of solar energy. The source of energy for the waves is the winds, blowing over hundreds or thousands of kilometers, whipping up the water. The physics is complicated, because the height of the waves can't be predicted from the frequency, and conversely. *Both* distributions are Rayleigh distributions[68] not unlike those we describe for wind in the "Wind-site Predictions." Additionally, the power in the waves when they reach shallow water is no more than about a quarter of the deep-water value, and the efficiency of converting low-head slow wave energy into electricity would be perhaps 25% to 30%. That is, we might expect about 25% of 25% (one part in 16) of the wave energy to be realized in the form of electricity.

The average deep-water wave power (greater than the electrical power that might be extracted) along the coasts is in the vicinity of 30 MW/kilometer.[69] At 25% conversion efficiency, it would take about 130 km of wave machines to produce 1000 MW, and the power (like wind power) would be weather-dependent.

Wave Energy in Realityland

There was a small, 24-foot long installation with floats that would rise and fall with the waves off the coast of New Jersey in the early 1900s that produced about 1.5 kW—equivalent to about 1.2 MWe per kilometer of coastline—about 20% of the maximum expected. If the entire coastline on both Atlantic and Pacific coasts were to produce power at that rate of 1.2 MWe/km, we would generate about 5800 MWe, less than 1.5% of the average US electrical energy production. At the full 8 MWe/km, the entire coastline from Mexico to Canada on both coats could only generate about 3800 MW, about 9.2% of our electricity. It is highly doubtful that environmentalists (or surfers or boat-lovers) would approve the project.

---

[68] C. L. Bretschneider, "Sea Motion," in Handbook of Ocean and Underwater Engineering, (McGraw Hill, New York).

[69] Peter Weiss, "Oceans of Electricity: New technologies convert the motion of waves into watts," *Science News* 159, pp. 234-236 (Apr. 14, 2001) gives 40-70 MW/km for a few excellent sites and 10-20 MW/km for southeastern US.

A 2001 research paper from Virginia Tech Alexandria Research Institute for a conference at Tufts[70] discusses wave energy and siting considerations. The author mentions some research projects, but presents no data on existing utility-scale devices. (There are none.)

A report with the auspicious title, "Results from the Work of the European Thematic Network on Wave Energy"[71] discusses some principles of wave machinery, but lists no useful ones. A report on the "Sea Dragon," which will consist of several 4-MW units is available at the same web site.

Tides

The causes of tides are more subtle. The gravitational pulls of the moon and of the sun cause very small perturbations in the sea level,[72] and the rotation of the earth causes those perturbations to move with respect to the continents. These "tides" are very small.

There are certain tidal basins, including the Bay of Fundy and the Rance Estuary (in France), where tides get very high. In such places, several effects contribute to the high tides.

One effect is that of *resonance*, a phenomenon that can be seen in any pool of water, such as a sink or bathtub. Push down slightly with the open hand and a wave moves away. When the wave reflects off a wall and comes back, lift up the hand. As the water starts to leave, push down slightly again. Before long, the height of the wave is much larger than the distance the hand moves. What makes it work is timing. Whether the water is coming in or going out, you are always pushing it the way it's moving, and adding energy to the system.

Resonance can happen only when the frequency of the driver (your hand) matches the natural frequency of the system (the water in its container). Resonance also requires that only a small fraction of the energy is lost in each cycle. Just as you can kill the vibrations of a guitar string by touching it with your finger, you could kill tidal oscillations by sapping too much of the energy.

Another phenomenon is the funneling of water. Suppose that westbound water has a tide that is no more than a centimeter high, but is a "wave" that is 500 kilometers in length. As it moves toward a continental coast, if the water gets funneled into a channel that is only 1 kilometer wide,

---

[70] George Hagerman, "Southern New England Wave Energy Resource Potential,"

[71] See http://www.wave-energy.net/Library/introLib.htm for several papers on wave energy.

[72] More correctly, the *gradients* in the gravitational pulls are responsible.

all of that excess water—the one-centimeter high wave—becomes a wave that is 500 times as high, namely, 500 cm, or five meters. Moreover, the wave speed increases, so the high tide comes in rapidly. The inverse of this funneling phenomenon is well known to Long Island Sound boaters. At the eastern end of Long Island, there is a narrow passage for the tide to pass through, known as *The Rip*. When the tide is going out, it is a real chore to be able to get a boat into the Sound. A similar phenomenon happens at San Francisco Bay.

Tidal Basins in Realityland

This discussion of tides is certainly incomplete, but our purpose here is merely to show why there are very few tidal basins of note in the entire world. High tide occurs twice a day. That is, for a short time, a tidal-hydro station would be operating at full head (far less than the hydraulic head of major hydropower dams). As the water runs out, the head decreases.

There is an existing 240-MWe (peak) power plant at the Rance Estuary in France that produces 500 million kWh per year, corresponding to a capacity factor of 26%.[73] There was a plan in 1961 to develop Passamaquoddy Bay (off the Bay of Fundy) between Maine, New Brunswick, and Nova Scotia, where 15-meter tides exist. It would have been a 230-MWe power plant, probably with a similar capacity factor of around 25%. There are, in fact, only a few such sites in the world, so the effect on worldwide energy production is obviously trivial.

Non-Solar Non-Source: Hydrogen

A few decades ago, it was common to speak of the "hydrogen economy," wherein hydrogen would be produced by electrolysis of water, with the energy being supplied by nuclear or fusion reactors. This would be a way to convert energy from stationary power plants into a form that could be transported. Everybody recognized that:
A. There are no hydrogen wells; hydrogen is not a *source* of energy;
B. Energy is *required* to produce hydrogen and that it would be impossible to get all of that energy back;
C. Storage and transportation of hydrogen are not trivial matters; and
D. While not a hazard beyond reasonable control, hydrogen is inherently more hazardous to handle than natural gas.

---

[73] Gordon L. Dugger, "Ocean Thermal Energy Conversion," in Douglas Considine's *Energy Technology Handbook* (McGraw-Hill, 1977).

Today, unfortunately, it is common to hear about a "hydrogen economy," wherein hydrogen is regarded as a *source* of energy. Cars will run on fuel cells, using hydrogen as an *energy source.* The evident plan (as conceived by writers who actually understand that we don't have free hydrogen around) is to use electrolysis of water to produce hydrogen. Briefly, but very incompletely, we simply insert some electrodes into water, feed in some current, and *voilá*, we liberate hydrogen gas. The experiment has probably been repeated in every elementary science class in the US for decades.

In this context, it is probably best to think of water as the waste product from oxidizing hydrogen. The chemical reaction is written as $H_2 + O_2 \rightarrow 2H_2O + \text{energy output}$. The energy output is heat if the hydrogen is burned, and some-heat, some-electricity if the hydrogen is used in a fuel cell. In energy terms water is already at the bottom of the barrel. In order to retrieve the hydrogen from the water, it is necessary to reverse the process—to feed in energy in order to break the water molecules apart to release the hydrogen. The chemical equation for that process is $\text{energy input} + 2H_2O \rightarrow H_2 \uparrow + O_2 \uparrow$, where the upward arrows indicate that the gases are released.

In an ideal world, the energy output from using hydrogen would equal the energy input used for electrolysis (or other process) to separate the hydrogen. We could set up a perpetual motion machine to use hydrogen to generate the energy to run the machine that liberates hydrogen. Not only is the perpetual motion machine physically impossible, but it also would accomplish no useful work to do anything else.

It is now time to look at some numbers. The heat content of hydrogen is 140 MJ/kg. We will show on page 168 that the typical efficiency of electrolysis is about 62%. That is, it takes about 226 MJ of energy to electrolyze water to produce one kg of H_2 that contains 140 MJ of heat content. To emphasize the point, we get 38% less energy out of the hydrogen than we used to get the hydrogen from the water. This is why we say that hydrogen is not a *source* of energy, but only a *carrier* of energy.

Again, the story is far from complete. Fuel cells typically are 60% efficient, meaning that 60% of that 140 MJ (namely, 84 MJ) can be usefully squeezed out of every kilogram of hydrogen. But if we use 226 MJ to produce the kilogram of hydrogen that has 140 MJ, and use the hydrogen in a fuel cell at 60% efficiency, we manage to squeeze 84 MJ output from 226 MJ input. The overall efficiency is 37%, even if we exclude the further losses occasioned by transporting the H_2 from where it is produced to where it is used.

We see that hydrogen is no more a source of fuel than the refrigerator is a source of milk or the electric socket is a source of electricity. A panel of the American Physical Society has analyzed the president's call for affordable hydrogen-burning cars by 2020. National Public Radio[74] calls the report a "sobering assessment." The APS group released a report March 1 that is deeply critical of President Bush's billion-dollar proposals for affordable, hydrogen-burning cars by 2020. The study says the technology needed to store hydrogen in a compact form for cars does not yet exist, and warns that expectations must be scaled back.

In the words of Peter Eisenberger, Columbia University physicist, and Chair of the committee, "It's not going to happen by 2020."

You wouldn't know it from press accounts, but the basic facts of hydrogen energetics have been known for at least a century, Why, then, has there been any recent interest in powering automobiles (for example) with hydrogen? There is the benefit that the byproduct of hydrogen oxidation (whether in a fuel cell or a fire) is plain old water. *It is important to understand that hydrogen addresses the problem of pollution, not of finding energy to run our civilization.*

It is also important to understand that using fuel cells requires more energy than not using fuel cells. The reason is simple. It always costs more energy to produce hydrogen than can be retrieved from the hydrogen.

Efficiency of Electrolysis

Governor Owens of Colorado organized a meeting called "<u>C</u>olorado <u>W</u>ind <u>A</u>nd <u>D</u>istributed <u>E</u>nergy" (CWADE, pronounced Sea Wade) at which practically everybody who spoke whined about not having enough subsidies.

One town father from Fort Collins discussed their plans to have a 100% gas-powered fleet of vehicles, using a mixture of natural gas and hydrogen. He showed a picture of the electrolyzer, and gave the specifications. The device uses 25 kW of electricity and produces 0.4 kg of hydrogen per hour. While I was busy calculating the efficiency, the speaker went on to claim that their electrolyzer operated at greater than 90% efficiency.

---

[74] National Public Radio, www.npr.org Morning Edition, javascript:getMedia('ME', '01-Mar-2004', 11, 'WM,RM')

I spoke to him afterwards and politely suggested that some salesman was jerking his chain. The heat content of hydrogen is 140 MJ/kg; therefore one hour's worth of hydrogen contains 56 megajoules. Dividing 56 million joules by 3600 seconds yields 15,500 joules per second (a.k.a. watts thermal). Put in 25 kW, get back 15.5 kW. That's 62% efficiency, not "over 90% efficiency." Moreover, the hydrogen energy is of lower quality than the electricity that produced it. (Electricity can be used for heat at 100% efficiency, or for motion at 90% efficiency. Hydrogen can at best be used at about 60% efficiency in a fuel cell.)

Using Solar Energy To Produce Hydrogen

Researchers have discovered how to electrolyze hydrogen from water using solar energy and PV cells that produce just the right voltage;[75] the efficiency is about 12.5%. The photovoltaic cells are made of GaInP and GaAs.

Other researchers have discovered algae that can produce hydrogen as a byproduct. They don't even mention the word *efficiency*, but we can make a reasonable estimate. One liter of algae-loaded water can produce 3 milliliters of hydrogen per hour in bright sunlight.[76] Let us assume that the liter is a cube, 10 centimeters on a side. At a solar intensity of 950 W/m^2, the rate at which solar energy enters the liter is 950 W/m^2 ×0.1 m × 0.1 m = 9.5 watts. The 3 ml has a mass of 0.26 mg; its heat content is 37 joules. The rate of production is therefore 37 J/hour = 0.01 watts. The efficiency is therefore about 0.1%.

Hydrogen can be used as a carrier of energy, and sunlight can be used to produce hydrogen by electrolysis or photosynthesis. The efficiency, however, is nothing to get excited about.

Delusional Economics

The utility has many expenses, including maintenance, repair, debt service, fixing downed power lines, running the equipment, health insurance and retirement benefits for employees, and of course fuel costs. It is not unusual for a utility to charge 10 to 15 cents per kilowatt-hour (the retail rate) for electricity delivered to your home, but to pay as little as 2 cents per kilowatt-hour (the wholesale rate) fuel cost for electricity from a baseload power plant.

---

[75] Robert F. Service, "A Record in Converting Photons to Fuel," *Science* 280, p. 382 (17 April, 1998).

[76] C. Wu, "Power Plants: Algae churn out hydrogen," *Science News*, p. 134 (Feb. 26, 2000).

When we hear the frequent claim that with a solar system on your roof, you can make the meter run backwards, it means that you would be selling electricity to the utility at the retail rate.   This perversion of economics is possible only when the heavy hand of government allows it or even demands it.

It is possible, using "smart meter" technology to make kilowatt-hour meters that can keep track of kWh delivered *to* the customer and kWh delivered *by* the customer, so that appropriately negotiated rates could be established.   After all, at the right price, the utility can indeed benefit from solar electricity developed on your roof.   But there is no way for a utility to survive if it has to buy and sell at the same price.

Chapter 17   Non-Subsiding Subsidies

It isn't always easy to find out how much the government is subsidizing whom. I am grateful to Glenn Schleede for ferreting out some useful information on energy subsidies.[77]

Lest there be any question about it, renewable sources receive the greatest subsidies, as shown in Fig. [1], taken from the Energy Information Administration.[78] The chart does not include local tax abatements and extra local utility income from people who love buying wind energy.

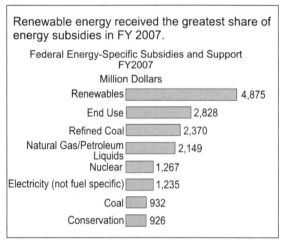

Source: Energy Information Administration, *Federal Financial Interventions and Subsidies in Energy Markets 2007* (April 2008).

Figure 1: Federal subsidies to various energy technologies. In 2007, renewable sources received about $ 4.9 billion, versus $ 1.3 billion for nuclear.

By Fig. 1, renewable energy gets about four times as much subsidy as nuclear energy. But nuclear power plants generate a whole lot more energy than renewable systems do. The EIA has therefore produced the table below that shows subsidies per unit energy produced.

---

[77] "How much does the Federal Government spend on energy-specific subsidies and support? Energy Information Administration of the Department of Energy at http://74.125.47.132/search?q=cache:FxoWfQvSfb8J:tonto.eia.doe.gov/energy_in _brief/energy_subsidies.cfm+energy+subsidies+us+department+of+energy&cd=1 1&hl=en&ct=clnk&gl=ca Thanks to Glenn Schleede for this link.

[78] www.tonto.eia.gov/energy_in_brief/images/share_of_subsidies_large.gif

Note the sudden shift as you go down the right-hand column. Conventional power sources get about a dollar per megawatt-hour (0.1 cents per kWh), but wind, solar, and "refined coal" get about $25 per MWh (2.5 cents per kWh). Of some interest is the last item in the table, "Refined Coal." Notice that it is different from "Coal" higher in the table. The item refers to research stations concerned more with CO_2 emissions than with producing power.

Rankings of subsidies and support based on absolute amount and amounts per megawatthour of generation differ widely, reflecting substantial differences in the amount of generation across fuels.

Subsidies and Support to Electric Production by Selected Primary Energy Sources

Primary Energy Source	FY 2007 Net Generation (billion kWh)	Subsidies and Support Allocated to Electric Generation (million FY 2007 dollars)	Subsidies and Support per Unit of Production $/MWh
Natural Gas & Petroleum Liquids	919	227	**0.25**
Coal	1,946	854	**0.44**
Hydroelectric	258	174	**0.67**
Biomass	40	36	**0.89**
Geothermal	15	14	**0.92**
Nuclear	794	1,267	**1.59**
Wind	31	724	**23.37**
Solar	1	174	**24.34**
Refined Coal	72	2,156	**29.81**

Energy Information Administration, *Federal Financial Interventions and Subsidies in Energy Markets 2007*, SR/CNEAF/2008-1 (Washington, DC, 2008).

Wind Subsidies

Many people argue that we need more subsidies for renewable energy. Let us have a look at some data. I have a PowerPoint file from a talk by a utility analyst who wishes to remain anonymous. His comment in the box below is particularly revealing.

Why the big push for Wind power??
TAX BENEFITS

The paper lists accelerated depreciation (30% for year 1), a production tax incentive ($1.90 per megawatt-hour) and various other tax incentives. For a hypothetical 1-MW turbine, the annual revenue generated directly by sales of electricity at 2.5 cents per kWh amounts to $54,750, but the first-year depreciation amounts to $300,000. All in all, the turbine produces a net gain of $316,000, amounting to over 14 cents per kWh.

In an article about a wind farm, Raabe[79] comments, "Platts data shows that wind power, *with federal tax incentives*, can be produced for $41 per megawatt-hour, compared to $43 for coal-fired plants and $48 for natural gas at current market prices." [emphasis added]

True enough. And with the right subsidies, power from coal could be produced for $0.00 per kWh, and two-carat diamonds could be given away in cereal boxes.

The Long Island Power Authority (LIPA) [NYT[80]] installed a 1-MW photovoltaic system in Farmingdale, Long Island for a mere $6.1 million, of which $4.1 million was due to Governor Pataki's generosity with taxpayers' money.

The 1-MW system is expected to produce "more than a million kWh per year"[80]. That's a fancy way of saying that it will effectively produce power 11.4% of the time, making the system the equivalent of a 114-kW power plant. The costs? $6.10 per installed peak watt; $53.50 per installed average watt. That's more than ten times as costly as the highly embattled Shoreham nuclear power station that was ultimately sold in the mid-1980s to New York for $1.00 before it could produce any electricity.

---

[79] Steve Raabe, "Energy-plan advocates hope wind is at their backs: Cost among hurdles in multi-city project", *The Denver Post* Sunday, October 26, 2003.

[80] John Rather, "Using Solar Power with LIPA's Aid," *The New York Times*, (March 16, 2003).

Chapter 18   Summary

Scientists and engineers have long understood sunlight and its uses. There is nothing new about the windmill formula, about the hydropower formula, about the production rates for biomass, or about the existence of PV cells. The intensity of sunlight—even that reaching the upper atmosphere—has been understood for well over a century. Efficiency has been a hot topic for two centuries. Using mirrors to concentrate sunlight has been known for millennia. Nor are tides, waves, and geothermal energy new to science.

There is an old adage that if something sounds too good to be true, it probably is. That adage is especially applicable to solar energy. For decades, there have been delirious proclamations that the world would soon run on solar energy (or in the current jargon, renewable energy). Those statements have always sounded too good to be true and, sure enough, have always been false.

Every year Lucy promises to hold the football so that Charlie Brown can do a place-kick. Every year as Charlie charges toward the ball, Lucy pulls the ball away at the last minute. Every year Charlie Brown lands on his back. Every year solar sirens tell us that solar energy is the answer to our problems. Every year people fail to learn from experience.

Hope springs eternal. The news media continue to publish and broadcast—unquestioningly—glowing stories about solar homes, wind farms, and cow manure, despite decades of failed predictions made by solar enthusiasts. Hope springs eternal.

The nuclear power industry had vociferous opponents long before the Accident at Three Mile Island Unit 2 in 1979. Nobody was harmed by the accident, except financially. If the accident were not costly enough, the Nuclear Regulatory Commission refused to let the utility operate TMI Unit 1 until 1985. Despite the sudden halt to the growth of nuclear power in the US, the 104 units in operation provide about 20% of our electricity, and have a system-wide capacity factor exceeding 90%. Nuclear energy is not a renewable resource, but the immense quantity available makes that question irrelevant. There is no shortage of nuclear energy.

Low-Tech, High-Tech

Broadly speaking, there are two ways to use solar energy.

In the traditional ways, the solar energy is collected by natural processes on earth. Sunlight evaporates water; we use hydropower. Sunlight produces chlorophyll; we burn trees and paper (from trees), and methane from human and animal waste. Sunlight causes the air to move; we put wind turbines where the winds are strong.

But we can also collect sunlight with man-made devices. Greenhouse-type solar heat collectors warm some homes and swimming pools. Focused-light devices (*e.g.,* Solar-Two and SEGS) can produce high-temperature heat to run steam turbines. Photovoltaic collectors produce electricity from sunlight.

Natural Collection & Storage of Energy

As it happens, we get most—indeed, almost *all*—of our solar energy from two of those natural sources. Biomass and hydropower together provide only about 7% of our energy. The average yield of firewood in New England's abundant forests is about 0.12 W/m^2, and that 1.2 W/m^2 is considered very high yield. The net yield from ethanol produced from highly fertilized corn yields a trifling 0.05 W/m^2 under the very best of conditions, but is usually negative instead. Despite the low energy intensity of biomass, it provides us with about 3.2% of our energy.

Wind ranks with biomass in terms of energy intensity, producing about 1.2 W/m^2 of land area in wind farms. Nevertheless, wind produces a minuscule 1.3 percent of our electricity. Wind power is currently the fair-haired child of the renewable-energy line-up, but has come to its stature through massive subsidies. Utilities offer their customers the opportunity to purchase "green" wind power for an *extra* several cents per kilowatt-hour, but generally would prefer to shun the low-quality power if given the chance to do so. For better or for worse, wind is the best solar energy available, aside from biomass and hydropower.

Collection & Storage of Energy by Manmade Devices

The solar energy collected by man-made devices involves higher energy intensity. Before it became the Keck Solar Observatory, Solar-2 produced year-round electrical energy at the average rate of about 3 W/m^2. LUZ International's SEGS project produces electrical energy at the average rate of about 11 W/m^2. Today's commercially available PV cells produce power at a year-round average of perhaps 25 W/m^2 if the load is continuously adjusted to keep the PV cells operating at their peak efficiency. Solar heat collectors for homes deliver heat at the year-round average rate of about 60 W/m^2.

Clearly, man-made solar collectors are greatly superior to natural ones, as indeed they ought to be; man has his own interests at heart. But they can collect only the solar energy that strikes them. To collect huge amounts of solar energy means building huge amounts—tens of thousands of square kilometers—of solar collectors. As a result, all such high-tech collectors, combined with all wind turbines, produce about one part in 400 of the electrical energy we use.

The high-tech direct-sunlight producers of electricity are expensive projects, and high-maintenance ones to boot. Mirrors and PV cells need frequent cleaning. The to-date total world production of PV cells is still in the range of a few tens of square kilometers, even three decades after the computer revolution began.

Non-Sources of Energy

Conservation and hydrogen have three things in common. Neither one is solar energy. Neither one is a source of energy. Both have adherents who claim that they *are* sources of energy.

Land Usage

Solar energy is inherently dilute, and inefficiencies in collection and distribution reduce the energy intensity even further. The more dilute the collection of solar energy, the larger the land area that is required for any given task.

To emphasize that point, let us look at the amount of land area that would be required to produce all of the 105 EJ of energy the US uses every year. The land area required would depend upon the efficiency of collection or, equivalently, upon the collected energy intensity in watts per square meter as shown in Fig. 52. If, for example, we could collect solar energy only at the rate of 0.4 W/m^2, it would require 100% of the US land area to collect all of our energy.

On the other hand, if we could collect solar energy at 20 W/m^2—twice the output of the field of parabolic reflectors in the Mojave Desert—we could get our energy from 2 percent of our land area; that value is just under the land area of Minnesota. (Minnesota is chosen here for its size, not for its sunlight.)

Even if it were possible to collect solar energy at 100% efficiency— though I emphasize that doing so is *utterly impossible*—the required land area would exceed that of Connecticut by some twenty percent.

On a map, Minnesota and Connecticut can be made to look small, even tiny if it suits the purpose. But the matter under discussion is the allocation of land area to solar projects. Imagine laying 4,400,000,000—4.4 *billion*—sheets of plywood, which is pretty cheap stuff, edge-to-edge, leaving no room for roads, houses, businesses, rivers, trees, or lakes. That's enough plywood to cover Connecticut.

Increase that by 20% to some 5.2 billion sheets of plywood, and you have enough collection area to collect all of the energy we use in the US—*if* the collection efficiency were 100%, and *if* our energy demand somehow didn't grow during the time all of those collectors were being laid out. The annual production of plywood is somewhere in the range of 0.5 billion sheets, only about 10% of our requirements.

Of course, some solar applications allow for multiple-purpose land use. For example, wind turbines do not conflict with hydropower obtained by drainage from that land, or with use of the land between towers for growing crops.

But plywood is not a solar collector of any kind, let alone one with 100% efficiency. We have simply ignored the problems of fastening the hypothetical solar collectors so that they don't blow away in the wind. We have made no provisions for cleaning the collectors of dirt or snow. We have made no provisions for delivering the energy, or for converting it to a useful form. We have made no provision for repair and maintenance. We have merely dreamed our way through the problems of energy storage.

Oh, and who is going to file the Environmental Impact Statement?

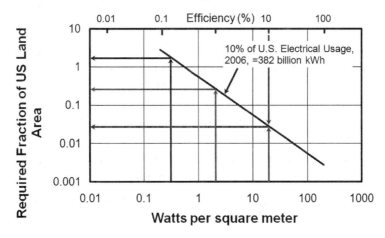

Figure 52: The required land area (heavy line) to produce all US energy (about 100 EJ/year) versus the energy intensity.

To find the required land area to get all US energy, find the productivity in watts per square meter, and go up vertically until the slanted line; then go horizontally to find the land area, as shown by the dashed arrows. The land areas of Minnesota (MN, 2.8% of US) and Indiana (IN, 1.2% of US)) are shown by the arrows on the left. The gross production of ethanol is about 0.2 W/m^2, and the net production (using the world's best equipment) is 0.047 W/m^2.

Environmental Opposition

In this dream world of 100% efficiency and plywood substituted for solar collectors, we still are faced with an enormous project and an environmental impact of more than biblical proportions. Highway projects, for example, are often held up for decades because the highway might destroy wetlands that amount to only the area equivalent to a few hundred or a few thousand sheets of plywood. Our project requires the land area equivalent to that of *billions* of sheets of plywood.

The easiest ways to increase solar energy would be to burn more trees and (with more difficulty) to put hydropower dams on all streams. Both attempts are met with vigorous political opposition by *environmentalists—* and not without some justification.

That is only the beginning. Environmentalists regularly oppose nuclear power plants and coal-fired power plants. They battle against natural-gas power plants and hydropower plants. They show up to protest geothermal power plants, wood harvesting, and high-intensity farming (with fertilizers and pesticides). To them, gas wells, oil wells, coal mining, gas pipelines, oil pipelines, electrical transmission lines are insults to the environment.

In a pro-wind article in the business section of *The Denver Post,* writer Steve Raabe comments on a proposal to build a huge transmission system to handle power from wind farms over a several state area.

"Backers acknowledge the ambitious 'wind energy pipeline' proposal is several years and billions of dollars from fruition.

"Plus, it faces *political opposition,* bureaucratic hurdles and a daunting challenge to raise the necessary money, estimated at $10 billion to $20 billion." [emphasis added]

> Steeve Raabe, "Energy-plan advocates hope wind is at
> their backs... ", *The Denver Post,* October 26, 2003

Oahu Follies

The main economic engine of Hawaii is Waikiki, a city famous for its beaches and other tourist attractions. Virtually all of the electricity is fed to the city on a single 138-kilovolt transmission line.[81] When a problem occurs, the city grinds to a halt until repairs are made.

Hawaii Electric Company (HECO) has a power-line right-of-way extending 1.19 miles (1.9 km) through conservation district land, with eight wooden poles presently carrying 46 kV subtransmission power lines. HECO requested permission to replace the eight wooden poles with eight taller (up to 110 feet, 33.5 m)) steel poles to enable them to install a second 138-kV transmission line to Waikiki, which would improve reliability for 54% of HECO's Oahu customers. The utility has already spent 13 million dollars on an environmental impact statement pertaining to the proposed replacement.

The wooden poles have been in place for some 30 years. HECO would paint the new steel poles to better blend into the natural background, landscape to partially screen them and locate some poles lower on the ridge to decrease the number of poles silhouetted above the ridgeline.

"It is not disputed that the project's most significant adverse impact is visual," says the City Council[82] in denying HECO's request. They noted that the power line would adversely impact the "spiritual aspects" of gathering plants for leis and traditional medicines on Wa'ahila Ridge.

---

[81] Alan Lloyd, Professional Engineer, long-time resident of Hawaii, private communication

[82] http://www.co.honolulu.hi.us/refs/bill/text/2002/r088.htm

In fact, environmentalists oppose every means of producing energy and every means of transmitting energy. Why would they feel good about huge energy farms? Why would they support transmission lines to carry electricity from sunny Arizona to New York? Why would they approve the use of hundreds or thousands of square kilometers of land to produce electricity? Why would they favor tens of thousands of miles of pipelines to carry hydrogen all over the country?

Make no mistake about it. The pro-solar crowd will eventually discover that solar energy projects that are big enough to be useful are big enough to be harmful to the environment. Meanwhile, they intend to kill all of the alternatives, all of the conventional ways of producing energy, all of the conventional ways of transporting energy, and all of the traditional ways of using energy.

The Echo Chamber

There is a problem with staying in friendly political circles. One person makes a proclamation and then somebody repeats it. Eventually the somewhat modified comment comes back to the person who originated it; he now believes it must be true because everybody is saying it, though in different ways. In this self-feeding echo chamber, fact yields to fiction, reality to delusion.

Journalists exacerbate the problem by acting as the powerful amplifiers of the echo chamber. They don't distinguish between conservation and sources of energy, between insulation and solar collectors, or between steady power from conventional power plants and stochastic power from wind turbines. They have no idea how many ways we use energy, nor where we use it. They have no idea that a car driving at highway speeds is consuming power at the rate of ten-to-twenty clothes dryers.

Schools of journalism teach their students to ask the traditional questions. Who? What? When? Where? Why? How?

Often the most important question is *How Much*? Schools of journalism do not teach their students to ask this question, let alone *how* to ask it. It is all too easy to copy an enthusiast's comment that a wind farm will produce enough power for 7,500 homes. How much power *in watts* will that project produce on the average? How many *watts per square meter of land area*? What is the expected capacity factor? How does the power compare with that of a nearby conventional power plant? How many wind turbines would be required to produce as much power as that conventional plant?

Conclusion

Solar energy, in its various forms, once ran the world. Primarily firewood, tallow candles, oil lamps, (non-electric) hydropower, animal power (from solar-powered photosynthesis), and a smattering of wind power provided enough for the then-small, non-industrialized world.

That was then. This is now.

The earth's population has long since exceeded the numbers that could be supported by those energy sources. As well, the agricultural technology existing a mere century ago could not possibly feed the world's billions.

For those who long for the good old days of a sub-billion population, it is useful to note that the only path to that end is for many billions of people now alive to die. We shudder to think of how they intend to accomplish the task.

The reality is that every time we heat something, we use energy. Whenever we shape anything, we use energy. Whenever we go anywhere, we use energy. Whenever we provide light, we use energy. Whenever we find or transmit information, we use energy. Every bit of our food and clean water, and every activity of treating sewage or of cleaning our air uses energy. It takes energy to build our roads and railroads, houses and skyscrapers, our clothes and shoes. It takes energy to make the insulation that keeps our homes from being drafty. Every piece of medical apparatus—CT scanners, x-ray machines, magnetic resonance imaging machines, operating room lights, and all the rest—uses energy. All of our drugs, from aspirin to antibiotics to cholesterol-lowering drugs, require energy to be produced.

As these pages have shown, some of that energy has come from solar sources, primarily the venerable ones, biomass and hydropower. Solar energy has always been and will always be a part of the overall energy picture. It is best described as a bit player that is destined to remain a bit player.

Energy efficiency has steadily improved for centuries. The least efficient lawn mower engine of today is several hundred times as efficient as Newcomen's original steam engine. Our houses of today require a minuscule fraction of the heat required for homes in colonial days. Fluorescent lights are hundreds of times as efficient as candles and whale oil lamps. Yet even if all modern efficiency improvements were retained while we tried to slip back to a solar-driven world, the solar energy available would fall far short of what is required to run the world.

A return to 100% reliance on solar energy, while using past technology would be utterly devastating, but probably nobody has that scenario in mind. Solar enthusiasts seem to favor a return to high reliance on solar energy while retaining every improvement in efficiency that has ever been accomplished.

Let us consider again an argument made in Chapter 6. Suppose that there is a very limited supply of available energy from conventional sources—petroleum, natural gas, coal, tar sands, oil shale, and fissionable nuclear materials—such that we will run out in some short time, say one century. If we manage to get 10% of our energy from solar sources, then we can extend that century by about 10 years. If we manage to get half of our energy from the sun, we would extend our high-energy century to two centuries. If we managed to get 90% by tomorrow morning, then we could extend our conventional energy to 10 centuries.

Ten centuries—one millennium—is a very long time compared to the lifespan of a human, but it is short compared to the duration of civilization. For example, in 21st century English, we still shun some Anglo-Saxon words as vulgar because William the Conqueror imposed French as the language of high culture on the English after the 1066 invasion.

Therefore, if we decide to settle on a solar future, a mere 10% would be about as effective as a Band-Aid on cancer. A 50% solar future would buy a century, and a 90% solar future would keep us in conventional fuels for a millennium, assuming that our conventional fuels would last only a century anyway.

Many times in this book, we have noticed that the only solar contributions of note have been the venerable ones—biomass and hydro. It is easy to use biomass, and always has been; one merely needs to burn grass, dung, tallow, or firewood. Hydro is much harder to use, but we may regard the technology as mature. But the relative ease in using biomass and hydropower is not the main reason for their usefulness.

Both biomass and hydropower represent *solar energy that has been stored*. As long as our woodpile lasts, we can grab a log and burn it *when we need the heat*. As long as we have water behind a dam, we can generate electricity *when we need it*.

This happy state of affairs does not—and never will—apply to wind, solar PV, solar/thermal-electric, direct solar heat, or any other possible solar scheme that does not include provision for energy storage. No matter how much power a wind farm generates in strong winds, we can't use wind-generated electricity when the wind doesn't blow. No matter how much power a PV or solar/thermal-electric system generates in the Mojave Desert on a summer afternoon, it will provide no electricity to New York City on a January night.

Appendix A. Units & Measurements

The international system of units (*Systéme Internationale*, SI) is used by scientists and engineers throughout the world, including the more civilized parts of the United States. The reasons for using SI are best elucidated in &&. It is of interest that all of the units in the English system are defined in terms of SI units, not the other way around.

This appendix presents straightforward information in SI units, and provides conversion factors for readers to convert *to* SI units. Readers who insist on converting *from* the SI system to their preferred parochial units will have to do that by themselves.

The metric prefixes are given in Table A1.

Table A1: Metric Prefixes

E (exa)	**10^{18}**
P (peta)	10^{15}
T (tera)	10^{12}
G (giga)	10^{9}
M (mega)	10^{6}
k (kilo)	10^{3}
m (milli)	10^{-3}
μ (micro)	10^{-6}
n (nano)	10^{-9}
p (pico)	10^{-12}
f (femto)	10^{-15}
a (atto)	10^{-18}

Many units have been defined for energy. Table A2 presents conversion factors. Note that the British Thermal Unit (BTU) is actually defined in terms of the joule by a 12-digit conversion factor.

Table A2 : Energy Conversion Factors

Multiply Number of ▼	By ▼ to get joules
Watt-seconds	1
British Thermal Units (BTU)	1055.05585262
Quadrillion BTUs (quads)	1.055×10^{18}
Kilowatt-hours (kWh)	3.6×10^6
Horsepower-hours	2.69×10^6
kilocalories (kcal)	4186.8
calories (cal)	4.187
Therms (=10^5 BTU)	1.054×10^8
Foot-pounds	1.36
Ergs	1×10^{-7}
Watt-years	3.16×10^7

Often used incorrectly as energy units are the heat contents of fuels. For example, we endlessly hear of nuclear weapon yields expressed in tons of TNT. Or, people will say that such-and-such project will displace a million tons of coal. Table A3 gives heat contents of fuels by mass, and Table A4 gives the heat content by volume. One kilogram of petroleum has a heat content of about 45 MJ/kg, and the same number holds approximately for all petroleum products. However, they have different densities. A gallon of propane weighs less than a gallon of gasoline, and therefore it has less heat content.

It is important to distinguish between the higher heat value and the lower heat value, the difference between them due to the heat of vaporization of water. Under almost all circumstances, either in heat engines or fuel cells, water *vapor* escapes, carrying with it the energy that converted the water to steam in the first place. The higher heat value (HHV) is the total energy per kilogram that is produced by the oxidation of the fuel; the lower heat value (LLV) is the amount that is actually usable. The EIA's tables give HHVs, but engineers generally use LHVs.

The most extreme case is that of hydrogen, for which the only by-product is water vapor. The higher heat value of hydrogen is 142 MJ/kg, but the lower heat value is 120 MJ/kg, some 15% less. From Table A3, the difference between HHV and LHV is about 10% for both methane and methanol, and about 6% for petroleum fuels.

Table A3: Heat Contents of Fuels (By Mass)

Multiply Number of ▼	By ▼ to get joules (HHV)	By ▼ to get joules (LHV)
Kg of crude petroleum	$42.5\text{-}45.4 \times 10^6$	41.2×10^6
Kg of gasoline	47.5×10^6	44.5×10^6
Kg of diesel fuel	44.8×10^6	42.5×10^6
Kg of coal	15×10^6 to 30×10^6	
Kg of coal (US average)	24.1×10^6	
Kg of drymatter (biomass)	15×10^6	
Kg of hydrogen (Not a *source* of energy!)	141.9×10^6	119.9×10^6
Kg of methane (CH_4)	55.5×10^6	50.0×10^6
Kg of methanol (CH_3OH)	20.0×10^6	18.0×10^6
Kg of ethanol (EtOH)	30×10^6	
Kg of propane	50.4×10^6	45.6×10^6
Pound of coal (average)	10.9×10^6	
Ton of coal (average)	21.9×10^9	
Kg of TNT	2.1×10^6	

Table A4: Heat Contents of Fuels (by Volume)

Multiply Number of ▼	By ▼ to get joules HHV
Barrels of crude oil	6.12×10^9
Barrels of aviation gasoline	5.326×10^9
Barrels of motor gasoline	5.542×10^9
Barrels of propane	4.047×10^9
Barrels of kerosene	5.982×10^9
Gallon (US) of gasoline	0.131×10^9
Gallon of ethanol (EtOH)	0.095×10^9
Cubic feet of natural gas	0.001092×10^9
Ton of TNT	4.2×10^9
cords of wood (white oak)	$31. \times 10^9$

The SI unit of time is the second; however, people frequently use other units of time. Everybody understands the length of a day or an hour; however, for calculations, one should use seconds. Table A5 shows easy conversion factors. (How many times would you like to multiply $60 \times 60 \times 24 \times 365.25$ to find the number of seconds in a year?)

Table A5: Time Units

Multiply Number of ▼	By ▼ to get seconds
Minutes	60
Hours	3600
Days	86,400
Years	$3.16 \times 10^7 \cong \pi \times 10^7$

The SI unit of length is the meter (*not* the centimeter, *not* the millimeter, *not* the kilometer). Americans use inches, feet, yards, and miles. Table A6 gives the conversion factors to convert lengths to meters. Note that the inch is *defined* to be 0.0254000... meters.

Table A6: Length Units

Multiply Number of ▼	By ▼ to get meters
centimeters	0.01
inches (definition)	.0254000000000000
feet	0.3048
yards	0.9144
kilometers	1000
miles	1.609

All areas, regardless of the shape of the surface, are ultimately found by multiplying length by length (and sometimes adding results of partial areas). Therefore, all areas in SI units are in square meters (m^2). Table A7 can be used to convert areas in common usage into m^2.

Table A7: Area Units

Multiply Number of ▼	By ▼ to get square meters
cm^2	1×10^{-4}
inches^2	6.452×10^{-4}
ft^2	0.0929
hectare (ha)	1.0×10^4
acre	4047
mi^2	2.59×10^6

Similarly, all volumes are ultimately found by multiplying length by length by length. Therefore, all volumes can be expressed in cubic meters (m^3); indeed, that is the only SI unit of volume. Table A8 shows the conversion factors to convert to m^3.

Table A8: Volume units

Multiply Number of ▼	By ▼ to get cubic meters
in^3	1.639×10^{-5}
gallon (= 231 in^3, by definition)	3.785×10^{-3}
liters	0.001
barrels	0.159

Table A9: Mass units

Multiply Number of ▼	By ▼ to get kilograms
pounds	0.4535
tons	907
metric tons	1000

We have but one sun, and its properties are known. Solar intensity values are given in Table A10. The figure of 1367 W/m^2 for sunlight reaching the earth's outer atmosphere was known within 10% over a century ago, long before satellites measured the intensity directly.

Table A10: Solar Intensity Values

Solar Flux	Watts/m^2 (of land area)
At earth's orbit	1367
At surface, noon, tropics, clear skies	950
Maximum conceivable 24-hour average, at equator, no clouds, at equinoxes	300
Albuquerque, New Mexico, yearly average	240
US, around 48 states, around-the-year, around-the-clock average	200
Hartford, Connecticut yearly average	160

Conversion of sunlight into useable energy is not always as efficient as some people would like to believe. Table A11 gives real and theoretical production intensities (in W/m²) for biomass, wind, and hydro.

Table A11: Solar Production Values

Solar Production	Watts/m² (of land area)
New England forests	0.12
US farm crops (edible portion)	0.11
Corn (whole plant)	0.75
Corn (edible)	0.25
EtOH from corn (gross)	0.195
EtOH from corn (net, best conditions achieved)	0.047
Biomass (in noon sun)	25
Sugar cane (whole plant, tropical conditions, plenty of fertilizer and pesticides)	3.7
Biomass (oceans, phytoplankton)	0.62 to .074
Biomass (maximum theoretical, average yearly production)	13.2
Hoover Dam (average power divided by collection area)	0.0014
All US dams (average power divided by collection area)	0.0049
Typical wind farm (with prevailing winds)	4
Typical wind farm (with winds from random directions)	1.2
Solar Two	3.2
SEGS	10.8

Table A12: Average [thermal] power consumption (2008) (by source)

	exajoules/year (EJ/year) 1998	exajoules/year (EJ/year) 2008	gigawatts (GWt) 2008
United States	100.6	112.4	3,560
World	402	495.2	15,700
US petroleum	38.8	39.2	1,240
US coal	22.8	23.6	747
US natural gas	24.1	25.1	794
US nuclear	7.46	8.92	282
US hydro	3.48	2.59	82
US biomass (includes farm & timber waste)	3.09	4.10	130
US geothermal	.346	0.378	12
US solar	.073	0.096	3
US wind	0.038	0.542	17

Electricity is clearly the most versatile form of energy, but there are no electricity wells. Table A13 shows the electricity picture in the US, both in billion kWh produced in 1998, and in around-the-clock average production in GW_e (= million kW_e = 10^9 W_e). Wind and solar combined produced 0.12% of our electricity—one part in 826. They produced 0.6% as much electricity as our much maligned nuclear power plants—one part in 167.

Table A13: Electrical Production 1998 & 2008 (US, by source)

	Generation billion kWh$_e$ 1998	Generation billion kWh$_e$ 2008	Average production (GW$_{es}$) 2008
Total	3620	4110.3	469.2
Utilities	3457	3966.7	452.8
Non-utilities	163	143.6	16.4
Coal	1873.5	1994.4	227.7
Nuclear	673.7	806.2	92.0
Natural gas	531.3	876.9	100.1
Other gas	13.5	11.6	1.32
Petroleum	128.8	45.4	5.18
Conventional Hydro	323.3	248.1	28.3
Geothermal	14.8	14.9	1.70
Wood	36.3	38.8	4.43
Waste	22.4	17.1	1.95
Wind	3.0	52.0	5.94 see footnote[83]
Solar (thermo-elec. & PV)	0.5	0.8	0.091

---

[83] In 2007, the US wind capacity was 16.5 GW, and wind generated 34.4 billion kWh, averaging 3.96 GWe; the overall capacity factor was 24%.

Wind is the fastest-growing energy source in the US, but only if you look at percentages instead of capacity. The growth from 1998 to 2007 was 14,800 MWe capacity (perhaps 3,600 MWe around-the-clock average). Direct solar power, whether from heat or photovoltaics, has a capacity factor of about 15 to 20 percent. That is, when advocates tell us the capacity, we should divide by five or six to get the expected annual average power. The capacity factor for wind can, in principle, be pretty much anything from 0% to 90%, depending upon the size of the generator fitted to the turbine. Typically, the capacity factor for wind generating systems is designed to be about 35%.

The capacity factors for much-maligned nuclear power are given in Figure 53. The worldwide average is 79.6% up from 71.2% that was achieved in 1998.

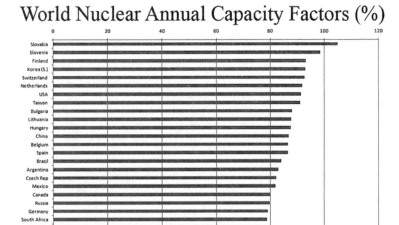

Figure 53: Nuclear capacity factors throughout the world.

The world-wide average capacity factor is 79.6%, up from 71.2% in 1998, with that of most countries exceeding 80%. Because of improved management, nuclear capacity factors in many US nuclear facilities are in excess of 91%. Slovakia is evidently running their four reactors at about 5% above rated capacity, and doing it continuously.

Appendix B. Device Physics

Work and Energy

The term *energy* is very abstract and very hard to define. Coal, oil, and natural gas are *sources* of energy, but are not energy themselves. Energy is actually a mathematical quantity that can not be held in a hand, put into a bottle, photographed, seen, carried, bent, shaped, cut, or otherwise handled.

Energy is the capacity to do work. Let us define what we mean by that term *work*, and then explain what is meant by the capacity to do work.

The simplest example of work is the lifting of an object. We push upwards with a force and the object moves up some distance. The work is the product of those two quantities— *work = force times distance*.

Now we will consider some variations on that theme. Suppose that we exert just enough force to move the object slowly upward. When the object reaches the top, it has some *potential energy*. Tied to another object with a rope that goes over a pulley, it can lift another body—do work on it.

Here's another variation. Suppose that we exert more force than just enough to move the object, effectively throwing the object upward. We will still calculate the work by multiplying the force we exert by the distance the object moves *while we are still exerting the force*. But when we reach the "top" the object still moves upward. The force we exerted was larger (else why did the object speed up?), so we have done more work. The object when at the "top" still has the same potential energy, but it's also moving fast. There is energy due to that motion called *kinetic energy*.

In this case, the work we did became partly potential energy and partly kinetic energy. We can also do work that results as heat, such as by pushing a block across a table as friction works against us.

The *capacity* to do work is not the same as the *ability* to do work. *Capacity* is a quantity. The gasoline in an automobile's gas tank has the capacity to do work, to move the car to higher elevation, to speed it, and to produce heat. However, in and of itself, it has no ability to do anything other than remain in the tank.

Heat Engines

A heat engine is any device that can convert heat to mechanical energy. Examples are steam engines, gasoline engines, diesel engines, and natural-gas turbines. In all cases, an expanding gas does work by pushing something, either pistons or turbine blades. But that gas could not expand if everything in its environment were at the same temperature. That is, the gas must be hotter than its surroundings.

There is an upper limit to the efficiency of a heat engine that depends only upon temperatures. That is, if we could make an engine that had no friction whatsoever and which wasted no energy whatsoever, it would still be impossible for the efficiency to be 100%. The reason lies in our surroundings. The ambient temperature is not absolute zero.

Another limitation on the efficiency of heat engines comes from the materials with which we build them. Higher efficiency would be possible if we could allow the temperature to rise up to, say, the temperature of molten iron. But that would destroy our engine.

The limiting efficiency of heat engines thus depends upon the high temperature of the expanding gas T_{Hi} and the low temperature of the surroundings T_{Lo}. The equation for the maximum thermodynamic efficiency is

$$\eta_{max} = \frac{T_{Hi} - T_{Lo}}{T_{Hi}} = 1 - \frac{T_{Lo}}{T_{Hi}}$$

wherein all temperatures are measured on the absolute scale. The temperature of our surroundings is about 300 K (kelvin) and the temperature of the expanding gas in heat engines is typically about 500 K to 550 K. For $T_{Hi} = 500$ K, the maximum possible efficiency would be 1–300/500 = 0.4, or 40%.

Insulation and R-value

The rate of heat flow through a wall depends upon the thickness of the wall, the area of the wall, the temperature difference across the wall, and the properties of the material that makes up the wall. (See Fig. 54.) The following two paragraphs are details for readers who may wish to understand the *R*-value of insulation used by manufacturers of insulation.

In practice, wall insulation is made up to certain thicknesses, so that one can define a *thermal resistance R*, or *R*-value to the insulation. Letting *A* represent the area of the wall, we have a simple equation,

$$\text{Heat Flow Rate} = \frac{A(T_{Hi} - T_{Lo})}{R} \qquad \text{Eq. 6}$$

Unfortunately, the R-value for commercial insulation is usually given in the English system of units. To use the equation, multiply the wall area in square feet by the temperature difference in degrees Fahrenheit. Divide by the commercial R-value. The answer is the heat flow rate in BTU per hour. Multiply that answer by 0.293 to get the heat flow rate in watts. Alternatively, if you measure temperatures in °C and areas in square meters, the appropriate r-value to use is the commercial one multiplied by 0.176.

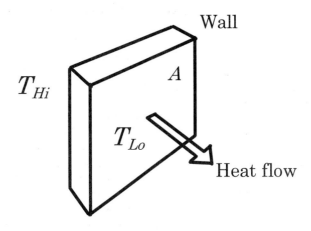

Figure 54: Heat flow through a wall.

The larger the area A of the wall, the more readily the heat flows; ditto for the temperature difference $T_{Hi} - T_{Lo}$ across the wall. The greater the thickness of the wall, the less easily the heat flows. Finally, the material of the wall has an effect as well. Good insulators restrict heat flow.

For example, the heat flow rate across a 200-ft^2 wall with an R-value of 15 when the interior temperature is 70°F and the exterior temperature is 10° is $(200)*(70 - 10)/15 = 800$ BTU/hour, or 234 watts.

The important things to remember about insulation are that the heat flow rate increases with increasing temperature difference across the wall and with increasing area of the wall. The heat flow rate is lower for thicker walls. We have not discussed air flow through a wall, but obviously the less air flow, the less heat the air can carry.

Windows

There is a corresponding procedure for understanding heat flow through windows, though it is a bit more complicated. If there is only one pane of glass, Equation 6 can be used; however, because the temperature varies across layers of air near the glass, the temperature on the inside of the glass is much lower than the room temperature and the temperature on the outside is much higher than that of the outside air, so the difference (T_{Hi} − T_{Lo}) must be measured directly on the glass itself. Nevertheless, it is common to assign an effective *R-value* for single-pane glass equal to 0.9 (commercial units) or 0.16 (SI units).

For double-paned windows, the effective *R-value* is approximately doubled to 2.0 (commercial value) and 0.35 (SI units). The main effect is that the lion's share of the temperature difference occurs across the air gap, so that the inner pane is at about the temperature of the room, and outer pane takes on the outside temperature.

There are two ways in which the insulating value of windows is increased further. One is to use a heavy gas like argon or krypton in the gap between the panes. The heavier the gas, the lower its conductivity. The other is to use extremely thin metallic coatings on the glass tailored to reflect infrared (IR). The coating has the dual characteristics of reflecting IR back into the room, but also of reducing emission of IR from the pane that is warmed by mere contact with the warm air in the room. This glass is called *low-e* (low emissivity) glass. Typically, a double-paned window with argon filling and *low-e* glass will have an effective *R-value* of about 3.8 (commercial units) or 0.26 (SI units).

Wind Power

Equation for Wind Power

For the benefit of interested readers, we derive Eq. 1 on page 66 for the power available from the wind.

Consider a column of air moving toward a wind turbine. It has cross-sectional area A and length ΔL (where the Greek letter Δ tells us to consider some small, arbitrary length), and therefore volume ΔV. If the density of the air is represented by ρ, then the mass in the column of air is $\rho \Delta V$. The air moves with velocity v, so its kinetic energy ΔE is $\Delta E = (1/2)\Delta Mv^2 = (1/2)\rho \Delta Vv^2 = (1/2)\rho A\Delta Lv^2$. We will define ΔL to be the length of air column that reaches the wind turbine in a short time interval Δt because of its speed v. Therefore, we can write the energy of the column as $\Delta E = (1/2)\rho Av\Delta t \times v^2 = (1/2)\rho Av^3 \Delta t$. Now we have an equation for the kinetic energy of an arbitrary amount of air. Big deal. We really care instead about the rate of arrival of energy, $\Delta E / \Delta t$, which is the power P_w in the wind. That is, $P_w = (1/2)\rho Av^3$.

The density of the wind can most easily be found from the knowledge that one mole of gas occupies 22.4 liters at standard temperature and pressure. There are, of course, two main gases in air, nitrogen (80%) and oxygen (20%). The mass in the 22.4 liters is 0.8*28 grams + 0.2*32 grams = 28.8 grams. The density ρ is therefore 28.8 grams divided by 22.4×10^{-3} m^3, which is 1.29 kg/m^3.

We will assume that the fan of the wind turbine is a circle of radius R. The area is therefore $A = \pi R^2$

The power output P_{out} of the wind turbine is the wind power P_w multiplied by the efficiency η. Therefore, we have

$$P_{out} = (1/2)\eta(1.27)\pi R^2 v^3 = 2.02\eta R^2 v^3$$

Any attempt at precision would be out of place here, as indeed it is when wind turbines are in operation, so we will round the 2.02 off to 2.

People who build wind turbine blades care how long they are, that is, the radius of the wind turbine; people who look at wind turbines are more likely to think of the diameter. We therefore give two equations for the wind turbine power, one using the radius, one using the diameter.

$$P_{out} = 2\eta R^2 v^3$$
$$= 0.5\eta D^2 v^3$$

The efficiency of an excellent wind turbine under ideal conditions will be about 50%, although most three-bladed wind turbines get up to only 45%. Moreover, in typical usage, the wind turbine achieves this power only at one wind speed. At higher speeds the efficiency is deliberately reduced by feathering the turbine blades. Using the 50% figure, we can arrive at a rule-of-thumb for the maximum power that an excellent wind turbine can achieve.

$$P_{out} = R^2 v^3$$
$$= 0.25 D^2 v^3$$

Almost all industrial wind turbines have three blades instead of two. Using two blades would make the turbine slightly more efficient; however, the turbine is dynamically more stable with three blades. (Technical note: the moments of inertia about any two perpendicular axes in the plane of the blades are equal.)

Wind-site Predictions

Our web site gets many questions from people who are interested in using wind turbines, but who have no idea of the many subtleties that are involved. The most important consideration is the distribution of wind speed at a given site. That information can be used to predict performance, as we show in this section.

The wind speed is never, say, 4.667221236825... meters per second. Therefore, the procedure is to round off wind speeds to the nearest 0.5 m/s. Figure 55 shows data taken from a wind farm in Kotzebue, located in a remote region of Alaska, just north the Arctic Circle. There were (for example) 490 hours during 1999-2000 when the wind speed was between 5.75 and 6.25 meters per second. Similarly, there were 585 hours when the wind speed was less than 0.25 m/s.

Usually, however, the data are more regular than those shown in Fig. 55. The Rayleigh distribution usually matches the data better than it does in this unusual case; however, the bad fit at low wind speed in Fig. 55 isn't particularly important because at those speeds, it makes precious little difference whether the turbine turns or not.

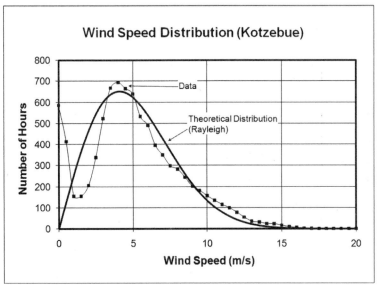

Figure 55: The wind speed at Kotzebue, Alaska (squares) and a simplified theoretical (Rayleigh) representation (heavy line).

The Rayleigh distribution[84] in Fig. 55 has a general shape, but the curve can be adjusted to lower or higher average wind speeds by adjusting one parameter V, as shown in Fig. 56. The value of V is $V = 1.13V_{avg} = \sqrt{2}V_{peak}$, where V_{peak} is the speed at which the curve reaches its maximum value.

---

[84] The quantity $(1/V^2)v\exp(v/V)^2\,dv$, where V is a reference velocity, gives the probability that the velocity lies between v and $v + dv$.

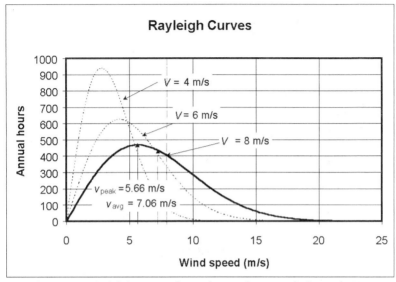

Figure 56: Rayleigh curves for various reference wind speeds *V*.

The next thing to do is to predict the annual amount of energy that can be obtained from the wind. The answer, of course, depends upon the size and quality of the wind turbine. Let us assume that the Rayleigh curve that fits our wind speed has a value of $V = 8$ m/s. We have a wind turbine that is capable of producing 100 kW_e when the wind speed is 11.5 m/s, and that (by design) the wind turbine will produce that power for all wind speeds up to 25 m/s, after which it will be turned off.

There are 199 hours during the year when the wind speed is 11.5 m/s (give or take 0.25 m/s), so that will contribute 19,900 kWh of energy to the annual total. Similarly, there are 287 hours a year when the wind speed is 10 m/s (± 0.25 m/s); however, the output power will be less than 100 kW_e. In fact, it will be 100 kW_e times the cube of (10/11.5), or 66 kW_e. Those 287 hours will therefore contribute 18942 kWh to the annual total. To find the total annual energy output, one repeats the procedure for every wind speed.

Given the same wind turbine, we could equip it with a 200-kW_e generator (which produces full power at 14.5 m/s) or a huge generator capable of unlimited power. See Fig. 57 to see the power output from each of the generators. We would then proceed to do the same calculations to find the annual energy output.

Three Hypothetical Generators on a Given Wind Turbine

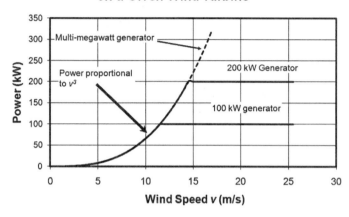

Figure 57: Power from one hypothetical wind turbine, equipped with either a 100-kW$_e$ generator, a 200-kW$_e$ generator, or a generator of unlimited power output.

The outputs of the generators are shown in Fig. 58 for various wind speeds. The shaded area under the curve represents the total energy output for a year for the 100-kW$_e$ generator. The unshaded area that lies above the 100-kW$_e$ curve and below the 200-kW$_e$ curve represents the annual difference between the energy production of the 200-kW$_e$ generator and the 100-kW unit, given the same wind turbine.

The annual output of the 100-kW$_e$ generator is 296,000 kWh, and that of the 200-kW$_e$ generator is 359,000 kWh. That is, the 200-kW$_e$ generator produces only 21% more energy in a year than the 100-kW$_e$ generator. The capacity factor—the ratio of average power to nameplate power—of the larger generator is 20%, but the capacity factor of the smaller one is 34%. If there were a 10-MWe generator attached, it would produce 392,000 kWh in a year, 32% more than with the 100-kW$_e$ generator. The capacity factor would be 0.45%.

It is extremely important to understand the wind speed at a given site. In our model above, if the reference wind speed were 7.5 m/s instead of 8 m/s, the annual energy for the 100-kW$_e$ generator would be 12% lower (261,000 kWh), and the capacity factor would be 30% instead of 34%.

The story doesn't stop there. From Fig. 56, it is apparent that even for the 100-kWe generator, most of the time—86% for this example—the wind speed is too low (i.e., below 11.5 m/s) to produce full power. The 34% capacity factor says much the same: most of the time, the power production is well below the nameplate power rating of the generator, even though there is a wide range of wind speed—11.5 m/s to 25 m/s—where full power is produced.

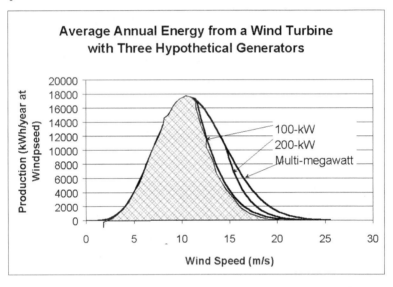

Figure 58: The electrical output in kWh for a wind turbine equipped with either a 100-kW$_e$, a 200-kW$_e$, or a multi-megawatt generator, for various wind speeds.

Area represents annual energy. (The bumps and wiggles are artifacts of the drawing program.)

Whenever the wind speed is below 11.5 m/s—that is, *most* of the time—the power output is not constant, but is proportional to the cube of the wind speed. This regime is the curved portion of the power curve in Fig. 57. If the wind speed fluctuates, then the output power fluctuates. When the wind speed is low, the power fluctuations have little effect on the power line. However, when the wind speed is higher, so that the output power is between 50 kW$_e$ and 100 kW$_e$, then the fluctuations require the output of conventional power stations to rise or fall in response. It is of interest that the output power is between half-power and full power about 15% of the time.

Hydropower

Equation for Water Power

Water has potential energy by virtue of being above some reference point. For a given incremental mass Δm of water, its potential energy ΔPE is $\Delta PE = \Delta mgh$, where g is the acceleration due to gravity, 9.8 meters per second per second (9.8 m/s^2), and h is the elevation, called the *hydraulic head* in Fig. 11 and subsequent text. The power (of the water) is the potential energy loss ΔPE divided by the time interval Δt during which the water moves down in elevation by h. That is, $P_{\text{water}} = \Delta PE/\Delta t$. Usually, however, one expresses the quantity of water in volume units, not mass units. The density ρ of water is 1000 kg/m^3. We have

$$P_{\text{water}} = \frac{\Delta PE}{\Delta t} = \frac{(\Delta m)gh}{\Delta t} = \frac{\rho gh \Delta V}{\Delta t} = \rho gh \frac{\Delta V}{\Delta t}$$

where $\Delta V/\Delta t$ = the rate of flow of water in cubic meters per second. The power output of the plant is the power of the water multiplied by the efficiency, η, which we take to be 85%. Inserting the numbers, we have

$$P_{\text{out}}(\text{watts}) = 8330 \times h(\text{meters}) \times \frac{\Delta V}{\Delta t}(\text{cubic meters per second})$$

In "Questions about Hydropower," page 8, we asked why water falling over a dam doesn't boil. If one kilogram of water descends 100 meters (about 300 feet) through a hydropower station, it generates enough energy to raise the temperature of one kilogram of water only about 0.23 °C. To raise one kilogram of water from room temperature (20 °C) to the boiling point (100 °C) requires about 343 kg of water to descend through that 100-m hydropower station.

Photovoltaics

PV cells as diodes

Photovoltaic cells are, in fact, rather amazing. But there's no magic involved. The devices have properties that can be measured by anybody who takes the time.

PV cells are made of dissimilar semiconductors placed in contact. So are solid-state diodes, devices that conduct current one direction but not the other. In fact, PV cells are diodes and that statement has implications.

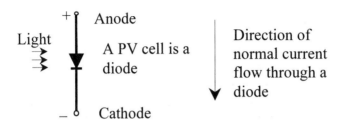

Figure 59: A PV cell is a diode.

When light shines on the cell, the anode becomes positive, *against* the normal direction.

Diodes are one-way devices for current, which flows in the direction of the arrow (See Fig. 59). That is, the current through the diode flows easily from anode—a *p*-type semiconductor—to cathode—an *n*-type conductor; current from cathode to anode is blocked.

When light shines on a PV cell, a voltage is generated such that the anode is positive. That is, current goes "backwards" through the diode, the direction it would resist conducting if a battery were attached to make it do so. The tendency for the current to leak back through the diode in its normal direction of flow—from the positive anode to the negative cathode—is real. In fact, the term *recombination current* is used to describe that very phenomenon.

It is important here to recognize that a PV cell actually generates a *current*, not a voltage. Although there is a voltage present, it is determined by something other than sunlight shining on the PV cell.

Here is what happens: sunlight dislodges electrons from their atoms, leaving positive ions behind. The positive spaces are called *holes*. As electrons hop from a neutral atom to a hole, leaving a hole behind, it appears as if the holes themselves are moving. This is the nature of the current in a *p*-type semiconductor. Sunlight produces *electron-hole* pairs; the electron goes one way, the hole goes the opposite, resulting in the *p*-type semiconductor becoming positive and the *n*-type becoming negative.

Diode Behavior of PV Cell

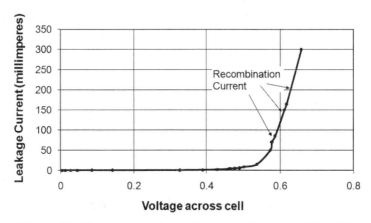

Figure 60: The current-voltage characteristics of a silicon PV cell.

Fortunately, the PV cell is a very non-linear device, as shown in Fig. 60. It conducts very little recombination current when the voltage is low, less than about 0.5 volts for the example shown in Fig. 60.

Suppose that the PV cell of Fig. 60 can generate 100 milliamperes when exposed to full sunlight. If the cell is not connected to a load, the generated current would exactly equal the recombination current; by Fig. 60, the voltage would be just under 0.6 volts. The efficiency would be zero, owing to the fact that (by design) no power is being delivered to do a load.

On the other hand, if we connected the PV cell to a load, some of the generated current would go through the load, and much less through the PV cell itself. For example, the voltage might drop to 0.5 volts. The recombination current (Fig. 60) would be 10 milliamperes, and the lion's share of the current—the other 90 milliamperes—would go through the load. The trick to using PV cells efficiently is to keep the voltage low enough that the recombination current is negligible.

In other words, the efficiency of a PV device depends upon the load to which it is attached. The actual behavior of a PV array will be discussed in figures 62 and 63.

Birdie, Birdie in the Sky

The diode characteristics have other implications for PV cells. Because they inherently generate low voltage, PV cells are normally placed in series to add the voltages, as shown in Fig. 61. It could conceivably happen, possibly through the courtesy of a bird, that one or more PV cells could be shaded. The light-generated current is always going "backwards" through the diodes, but when a PV cell is shaded, it generates no current and merely blocks that passage of current generated by the other cells. Fortunately, the PV cell is not a good diode; the voltage need not be very high before it will permit current to pass through it the wrong way.

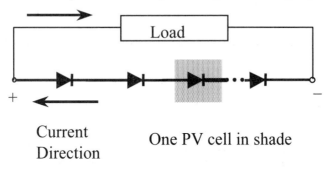

Figure 61: A PV array with one PV cell in shade.

I borrowed an 18-cell PV array from the student labs at the University of Southern Colorado. (The cells are amorphous silicon, cheaper than, but not as efficient as crystalline silicon wafers.) The characteristics of the device when connected to an adjustable load are shown in the upper curve in Fig. 62. When the load resistance is high, the current is very low and the voltage is high, as shown at the lower right of Fig. 62. The power—the product of high voltage (22V) and zero current (0)—is zero. That is, the efficiency is zero (or near zero) when either the PV cell is connected to a load resistance that is either too high or too low. The maximum efficiency occurs when the load resistance is such that the "operating point" is near the knee of the curve of Fig. 62, as shown by the tip of the arrow.

PV output

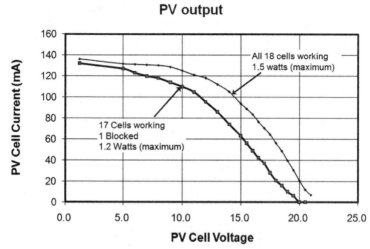

Figure 62: The output from a PV array with all 18 cells exposed to full sunlight (upper curve) and with one cell shaded.

When the load resistance is very low, the effect of sunlight is merely to drive electrons around a loop that does not inhibit the flow. The current is high (136 mA), but the voltage is zero, so, again, the power is zero. When everything is adjusted just right, the power is maximized at about 13.6 volts, 110 mA, (tip of arrow) where the output power is 1.5 watts. The efficiency of the unit is about 5%.

The lower curve in Fig. 62 shows what happens when one of the 18 cells is shaded by a piece of wood placed over the cell. In this case, the maximum power output is reduced from 1.5 watts to 1.2 watts, a 20% decrease caused by a 5.6% reduction in the number of cells exposed to sunlight. The efficiency of the 18-cell array, that is, has dropped from 5% to 4% because of that one blocked cell.

Power output

It is interesting to seek the point where maximum power is produced. Figure 63 shows a hyperbolic line where the power PV = constant = 1.45 watts. That curve just grazes the actual output curve right at what might be called the knee of the output curve, very close to the point where we just found 1.46 watts produced.

Not that anybody wants to produce less than the maximum power, but Figure 63 shows that there are two configurations that will do it for 0.7 watts. These are the points of intersection between the 0.7-watt curve and the actual output curve. That is, we can get 0.7 watts either at 39.5 mA (17.7 V) or 131 mA, 5.3 volts.

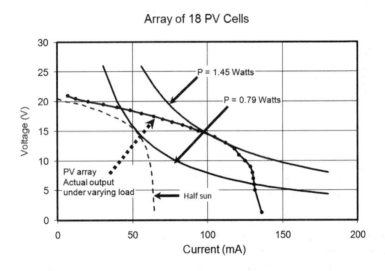

Figure 63: The current-voltage characteristics ("Actual output") of a PV cell array consisting of 18 small PV cells in series placed in full sunlight.

Voltage and current were measured for about 20 different resistances placed across the terminals of the PV cell. Also shown are two other curves representing constant power at 1.45 watts and 0.7 watts.

Now let us imagine that the sun's intensity is reduced to half, either because of cloud cover or because the sun is lower in the sky. What will the output of the PV cell be then? Actually, the *left* side of the output curve looks pretty much the same; that is, the output voltage is unaffected for low current.

However, the knee of the curve shifts toward the left, and the reason is not hard to find. With half the amount of sunlight, half as many electrons are freed to produce a current. The short-circuit current (the value of the current when the external resistance is very low, represented by the hanging tail near 135 mA in Fig. 63) is directly proportional to the sun's intensity. The result of reduced sunlight is therefore only that the knee moves leftward.

Our job is to find the configuration that will give maximum power at this new situation with only half the solar intensity. Again, the hyperbolic curve for constant power, such as those for 1.45 and 0.7 watts, will intersect the output curve in two places, except for the case of maximum power, where there will be only one point of intersection. The dashed line in Fig. 63 shows the expected output at half the solar intensity. Note that the power is 0.79 watts, which is a bit more than half of 1.45 volts. The voltage at which the maximum power occurs is a little higher than that for maximum power at full solar intensity.

Power to the People!

It is normal for the delivered power to depend upon the voltage source, whether the source be hydropower, coal, or other fuel. If a customer demands more power, the demand is immediately felt at the generator, where the rotation rate diminishes. Immediately, the generator is brought back up to speed by the application of more steam, more natural gas (turbines), or more water (for hydro).

When the demand for PV power increases, however, the PV cell can do nothing to help, short of begging the sun for more light. Of course, the power output will *decrease*, because the PV array will already be operating at maximum power.

Demand Instability

Figure 63 shows real data for the 18-cell PV array, and a hyperbolic line representing the voltage and current requirements to generate 1.45 volts. They intersect at one point. What happens when there is a sudden demand for more power? This can only happen when the resistance of the load decreases, and the current increases. The power output of the PV array necessarily decreases.

In other words, a demand for increased power results in a decreased supply of power, resulting in a stronger demand for power, resulting in even less power. Overall, then, there is *demand instability*. When more power is demanded, the PV cell can't supply it; worse yet, the PV power *decreases*.

Demand instability is what happened with the Great Northeast Blackout of 1965. With no ability to compensate for increased demand (due to the malfunction of one relay), the system responded by reducing power (circuit breakers removing power plants from the grid).

Less Light, Less Power

Figure 63 shows the output of the 18-cell array in full Pueblo, Colorado, sunlight and in half sunlight, as one might have on a hazy day (one where the sun appears to be somewhat lost in haze, but there are still distinct shadows). Half sunlight can also occur if the array is 60° from facing the sun directly (morning conditions). The largest effect of half-sun conditions is a reduction of the current at which maximum power occurs; the optimum voltage is basically unaffected.

The terms *solar cell* and *solar battery* give the wrong impression. Unlike batteries, PV collectors do not store energy. The instant the PV collector is shaded, it stops producing electricity.[85] It is important to recognize that if PV cells are to provide electricity when the sun is not shining, the energy must be stored, somewhere, somehow.

---

[85] For that matter, it is useful to remember that the electrical grid is not a storage device. At all times, the electricity being generated is being used somewhere.

References

Annual Energy Review 2008, Energy Information Agency of the Department of Energy, available from US Government Printing Office. Visit www.eia.doe.gov, and search for aer2008 to download a PDF file.

Beckmann, Petr, *Access to Energy,* Oct. 1978.

Berman, Daniel M. and John T. O'Connor, *WHO OWNS THE SUN?: People, Politics, and the Struggle for a Solar Economy* Chelsea Green Publishing Company, White River, VT 1996.

Blackburn, John O., *THE RENEWABLE ENERGY ALTERNATIVE: How the United States and the World Can Prosper Without Nuclear Energy or Coal* Duke University Press, 1987.

Bretschneider, C. L., "Sea Motion," in *Handbook of Ocean and Underwater Engineering,* Myers, John J., Carl H. Holm, editors, McGraw Hill, New York, 1969.

Bryan, Ford R. *Henry's Attic,* Ford Books, Dearborn, MI, 1995.

Brower, Michael, COOL ENERGY: Renewable Solutions to Environmental *Problems,* **The MIT Press, Cambridge, MA, 1992.**

Brown, Lester R., Christopher Flavin, and Sandra Postel, *SAVING THE PLANET: How to Shape an Environmentally Sustainable Global Economy* W.W. Norton, New York, 1991.

Bryson, John E. President, Calif. PUC, *FINANCING THE SOLAR TRANSITION: A Report To The California State Legislature,* Calif. PUC Jan 2, 1980.

Commoner, Barry, Howard Bokensenbaum, and Michael Corr, eds. ENERGY AND HUMAN WELFARE—A CRITICAL ANALYSIS, *Volume II: Alternative Technologies for Power Production,* **Macmillan Information, New York, 1975.**

Commoner, Barry, "Prepared Statement of Barry Commoner" for Birch Bayh's hearings on biofuels, *Alcohol Fuels Hearings* (1978).

Considine, Douglas M., P.E., Editor, *Energy Technology Handbook,* (McGraw-Hill, 1977).

Ehrenreich, H., Chairman, *Solar Photovoltaic Energy Conversion: Principal Conclusions of the American Physical Society Study Group on,* American Physical Society, January, 1979.

Ehrlich, Paul R. and Anne H. Ehrlich, THE END OF AFFLUENCE, *A Blueprint for Your Future,* **(Rivercity Press,1974).**

Ehrlich, Paul R. & Anne H. Erhlich, *HEALING THE PLANET: Strategies for Resolving the Environmental Crisis*, Center for Conservation Biology, Stanford University, 1991.

Energy and Power, Scientific American offprint book, W.H. Freeman (1971).

Hayes, Denis, RAYS OF HOPE: *The Transition To A Post Petroleum World* (W. W. Norton & Company, 1977).

Hore-Lacy, Ian, *Nuclear Energy in the 21st Century*, (World Nuclear University Press, London: Elsevier, Massachusetts, 2006).

Hubbard, H. M., "Photovoltaics Today and Tomorrow," *Science* **244**, pp. 297–304 (21 April 1989).

Huff, Darrell, *How to Lie with Statistics*, (W.W. Norton, Inc., New York, 1954).

International Energy Outlook 2008, Energy Information Agency of the Department of Energy, available from US Government Printing Office.

Inventory of Electric Utility Power Plants in the United States 1999, DOE/EIA-0095(99)/1, September 2000. Available from the US Government Printing Office.

Jackson, Barbara Ward and René Dubos, *ONLY ONE EARTH: The Care and Maintenance of a Small Planet*, W.W. Norton & Company, New York, 1972.

Keyes, John, *THE SOLAR CONSPIRACY: The $3,000,000,000,000 game plan of the energy barons' shadow government*, Morgan and Morgan Publishers, Dobbs Ferry, NY, 1975.

Lovins, Amory, *SOFT ENERGY PATHS: Toward a More Durable Peace* Balinger Publishing Co., Cambridge, MA, 1977.

Lovins, Amory, "Tough Lovins," *The Weekly Standard,* p. 6, June 4, 2001.

Meinel, Aden E. and Marjorie P. Meinel, *Applied Solar Energy,* Addison-Wesley Publishing Co., Reading, MA, 1976.

Naar, Jon, **DESIGN FOR A LIVABLE PLANET**, (Harper and Row, 1990).

Nader, Ralph, 1997: *Frontline* (PBS Broadcasting, 4/22/1997).

Oppenheimer, Michael, and Robert Boyle, *DEAD HEAT: The Race Against the Greenhouse Effect* (Basic Books, New York, 1990).

Reese, Ray, THE SUN BETRAYED: *A Report on the Corporate Seizure of U.S. Solar Energy Development,* (South End Press, P.O. Box 68, Astor Station, Boston, 1979).**

San Pietro, Greece, and Army, eds., *Harvesting the Sun: Photosynthesis in Plant Life*, (Academic Press, New York, 1967).

Robert F. Service, "A Record in Converting Photons to Fuel," *Science* **280**, p. 382 (17 April, 1998).

Statistical Abstract of the United States, available from US Government Printing Office.

Train, Russell, Chairman, CHOOSING A SUSTAINABLE FUTURE: *The Report Of The National Commission On The Environment,* **(Island Press, Washington, D.C. 1993).**

C. Wu, "Power Plants: Algae churn out hydrogen," *Science News*, p. 134 Feb. 26, 2000.

Wind Energy: The Case Of Denmark, Center for Politiske Studier, September, 2009.

Web Sites

http://www.cato.org/pubs/pas/pa-241.html

http://www.commondreams.org/views01/0708-05.htm, Amory B & Hunter L. Lovins, "Too Expensive and Unacceptably Risky, Nuclear Power was Declared Dead Long Ago. So Why Would We Resurrect It?" (Dec. 10, 2001).

http://www.eia.doe.gov

http://www.energyadvocate.com

http://www.energy.ca.gov/wind/windfacts.html

http://www.energy.ca.gov/wind/wind-html/95_wind_report.html

http://www.epa.gov/globalwarming/publications/actions/state/wa/mitigatef. html

Browner 1998: http://www.epa.gov/oppeoee1/globalwarming/actions/clean-energy/sol/browner_498.html

http://www.es.wapa.gov/pubs/esb/97Oct/at_roof.htm

http://www.greenpeaceusa.org/media/factsheets/windtext.htm

http://www.jxj.com/magsandj/rew/1999_04/comingofage.html (Christopher Flavin & Seth Dunn, 1999)

http://teamhouse.tni.net/janebio.htm (Jane Fonda, 2000)

http://www.nrel.gov

http://www.nrel.gov/data/pix/searchpix.html

http://www.nrel.gov/documents/profiles.html

http://rredc.nrel.gov/solar/#archived.

http://people.cornell.edu/pages/tg21/usgs.html

http://www.rmi.org/sitepages/pid189.php (Amory Lovins, 2001)

http://www.tidalelectric.com/events/archives/archive0298.html (Gore $48 billion)

Worldwatch (1996): http://www.worldwatch.org/alerts/pr960814.html

http://www.worldwatch.org/alerts/010517.html (Hydrogen as *source* of energy)

http://www.renewableenergyworld.com/rea/news/article/2009/08/ge-energy-to-acquire-offshore-wind-turbine-supplier-scanwind-of-norway

Index

About the Author

Howard Hayden is a Professor Emeritus of Physics from the University of Connecticut.

A Colorado native, he entered the University of Denver as an engineering major, but soon discovered that he wasn't temperamentally suited to all that reality. He switched to physics and went on to earn his B.S., M.S., and Ph.D. at DU.

On receiving his Ph.D., he spent a 32-year academic career at the University of Connecticut He did accelerator-based atomic physics, including measurements of cross-sections for various processes, measurements of energy loss in atomic collisions and of lifetimes of excited states, beam-foil spectroscopy, and ion implantation.

He also repeated the famous Trouton-Noble experiment, but with 100,000-times greater sensitivity. For nearly a century, it had been believed that the Trouton-Noble experiment contradicted classical physics and leant support to Einstein's special relativity theory, but Hayden proved that the experiment did not contradict either classical theory or Einstein theory. Therefore, the original experiment was essentially meaningless, and so was Hayden's. Still, he succeeded in getting the work published.

Hayden has a long-standing interest in energy, stemming from before the OPEC oil embargoes of the 70s. Presently, he publishes a monthly newsletter, *The Energy Advocate*, which in August 2009 began its 14th year of publication.

Vales Lake Publishing

Vales Lake Publishing
P.O. Box 7609
Pueblo West, CO 81007-0609
(719) 547-7805
fax: (719) 547-7819
SAN: 2 5 4—2 5 3

Please visit www.valeslake.com to obtain books on energy, climate, mathematics, probability, relativity, electromagnetic radiation, and beaded jewelry. We have numerous *Golem Press* books written by, and translated by the late Petr Beckmann.

We have recently published these books on climate:

- Howard C. Hayden, *A Primer on CO$_2$ and Climate*
- Dr. Craig D. Idso, *CO$_2$, Global Warming and Coral Reefs: Prospects for the Future*
- Dr. Craig D. Idso & Dr. Sherwood B. Idso, *CO$_2$, Global Warming and Species Extinctions: Prospects for the Future*

We also publish the monthly energy newsletter *The Energy Advocate*. Please contact us for a sample